AGS

Punctuation, Capitalization, and Spelling

by
Bonnie L. Walker, Ph. D.

AGS®

American Guidance Service, Inc.
4201 Woodland Road
Circle Pines, MN 55014-1796
1-800-328-2560

Printed in the United States of America

ISBN 0–7854–0946–7 (Previously ISBN 0–88671–537–7)

Product Number 90842

A 0 9 8 7 6

Contents

Periods

➤ A period (.) is an end punctuation mark. The most common use of a period is to mark the ends of sentences.

Sentences that are statements, commands, and requests end with periods.

Statement   Victor bowls every Saturday.

Command   Meet Victor at the bowling alley.

Request   Please be there by 10 o'clock.

A Add a period at the end of each sentence. On the line, identify each sentence as a statement, command, or request.

_____   **1.** Cats are a popular pet in the United States

_____   **2.** Do not let the cat outside

_____   **3.** Cats have a good sense of balance

_____   **4.** Please feed the cat

_____   **5.** Stay away from the cat

_____   **6.** Take the cat to the veterinarian, please

_____   **7.** Some people say cats have nine lives

_____   **8.** Please be sure the cat has fresh water

_____   **9.** Our cat has a colorpoint coat with its face, paws, and tail darker than its body

_____   **10.** Make sure the kittens stay in their box

B Add a period at the end of each sentence in this paragraph.

Some people think growing African violets is difficult

That's not true You just have to remember a few simple rules

Keep the soil moist Do not overwater them Try to avoid getting

the leaves wet African violets need light However, do not

put them in direct sunlight Remember to fertilize them

Then you will have beautiful African violets

➤ **Initials:** An initial is the first letter of a person's name. Initials are followed by periods.

> T. S. Eliot (Thomas Stearns Eliot)
> W. E. B. Du Bois (William Edward Burghardt Du Bois)

➤ **Abbreviations:** An abbreviation is a shortened form of a word or phrase. Some abbreviations are followed by periods. Others are not. If you are not sure whether an abbreviation should have a period, check a dictionary.

Usually, you do not use abbreviations when writing a composition. However, some abbreviations are acceptable in compositions. See the chart for some of the acceptable abbreviations.

Acceptable Abbreviations	
Titles before a name:	Dr. Kurani, Mr. Martinez, Mrs. Lee
Titles and degrees after a name:	Carlos Ortiz, Jr.; Michael O'Connor, Sr.; Marietta Winthrow, Ph.D.
Time designations:	A.D. 485, 26 B.C., 3 P.M., 4 A.M.
Acronyms:	FBI (Federal Bureau of Investigation), NFL (National Football League), NATO (North Atlantic Treaty Organization)

A Write the initial or abbreviation for the underlined word or words. Use periods where needed. Check a dictionary if necessary.

Western <u>Avenue</u> _____

<u>September</u> 15 _____

<u>General</u> Rodriguez _____

15 <u>kilometers</u> _____

one <u>inch</u> _____

Anchorage, <u>Alaska</u> _____

<u>Thursday</u> _____

Washington, <u>District of Columbia</u> _____

<u>National Aeronautics</u>

<u>and Space Administration</u> _____

Susan <u>Brownell</u> Anthony _____

B Underline each abbreviation in the paragraph. Then rewrite the paragraph on your own paper. If the abbreviation is acceptable in a composition, add periods where necessary. If the abbreviation is not acceptable, write out the word.

     This Jan we visited Washington, D C, our nation's capital. On Mon we toured the FBI building. On Tues we walked down Sixteenth St to Pa Ave to get to the White House. I hoped we would see the Pres and First Lady, but we did not. Our last day in Wash was Jan 15. That is the birthday of Dr Martin Luther King, Jr, so we went to the Lincoln Mem, where he gave his famous "I Have a Dream" speech.

Decimal Points

➤ A decimal point (.) looks just like a period. Decimal points are used in mathematics. We also use them to express amounts of money.

$14.38   The decimal point separates the dollars from the cents.

A Rewrite each expression using numbers and decimal points. Remember to use the dollar sign ($) with amounts of money.

1. thirteen dollars and twenty cents   _____

2. two hundred dollars and three cents   _____

3. nineteen dollars and eighty-eight cents   _____

4. three dollars and five cents   _____

5. six point five   _____

6. nine dollars and forty-six cents   _____

7. fourteen dollars and ninety-two cents   _____

8. a dollar sixty   _____

9. seventeen hundred dollars   _____

10. ninety-nine point four   _____

B Add periods or decimal points wherever needed in the following sentences.

1. Dr Anna L Cortesi has an office on Eastern Ave in Tucson, AZ

2. Both Luca and Su Lin have a grade point average of 3 9 on a 4 point scale

3. The headquarters of the FBI is in Washington, D C

4. I have an appointment with Mr Robert L Steiner at 2:30 P M on Fri, Sept 1

5. Richard M Nixon resigned the presidency on Aug 9, 1974

6. On Aug 21, Kristen will be 14

7. On the scale, one inch equals 250 miles

8. My parents celebrate their tenth anniversary on Nov 10

9. Robert P Warren won the Pulitzer Prize for his novel *All the King's Men*

10. Booker T Washington was the first principal of the Tuskegee Institute in Alabama

➤ A question mark (?) is used at the end of a sentence that asks a question.
  Do you like reading the comics in the newspaper?
  Which comic strip is your favorite?

➤ Use either a question mark or a period after a polite request.
  Will you please mail this letter for me.
  Will you please mail this letter for me?

➤ Sometimes writers use question marks to express uncertainty.
  I wonder what will happen next?

A Find the end of each sentence in this paragraph and mark it with a period or a question mark.

   Many high school students plan to go to college Do you If so, you have many choices Do you prefer a junior college or a university Either choice is a good start toward a higher education

B Change each of the following statements to a question. Add the appropriate mark of end punctuation. Add helping verbs if needed.

Example: Frank walked home from school.
           Did Frank walk home from school?

1. Breakfast is ready.

   _____

   _____

2. We are having cereal and fruit.

   _____

   _____

3. Everyone wants orange juice.

   _____

   _____

4. You may have a bagel and cream cheese.

   _____

   _____

Exclamation Points

➤ An exclamation point (!) is used after sentences and words that express strong feeling. You can also use an exclamation mark to emphasize your point!
   What a lovely day this is!   I'm lost!   Oh, boy!
   Wow! Wonderful!   No!

A Add the appropriate mark of end punctuation to each sentence.

1. Did you see the movie on TV last night

2. It starred George Clooney

3. He's great

4. He also is a cast member on a TV series

5. Have you seen him in that show

➤ In some situations you can use a question mark or an exclamation point. It depends on the exact idea you wish to express.
   What is going on here? (question to be answered)
   What is going on here! (expression of feeling)

What's the difference?

Using a question mark or an exclamation point can change the meaning of a sentence. How does the punctuation change the meaning of the following examples?

Example 1:   "I am leaving in about five minutes," said Claudia.
         "What?" Alice replied.

Example 2:   "I am leaving in five minutes," said Claudia.
         "What!" Alice replied.

B Add the appropriate mark of end punctuation at the end of each sentence.

   Where's the party I can hear a band playing off in the distance

   It sounds like a good party I'd sure like to be there Wouldn't you

   Yes Let's go It is Bob Turrelli's party, and he invited us

Punctuating Interjections

➤ Use an exclamation point (!), a question mark (?), or a comma (,) after an interjection.

➤ An interjection is a word or phrase that expresses feeling.

| Oh! | Ah! | Great! | Oh, no! | Hurrah! |
| Help! | What? | Why? | Oops! | Ouch! |

Study these examples carefully.

Oh, did you already have dinner?
A comma indicates less feeling. A comma is NOT a mark of end punctuation. The word following it is not capitalized.

Oh! Did you already have dinner?
An exclamation point shows stronger feeling. It is a mark of end punctuation. The word following it must be capitalized.

Oh? Did you already have dinner?
A question mark indicates the speaker is using the interjection to ask a question. A question mark is also a mark of end punctuation. The word following it starts a new sentence and must be capitalized.

 Recopy these sentences. Add a mark of punctuation after each interjection and at the end of each sentence. Capitalize the first word that follows the interjection if necessary.

1. oh, no please don't turn off the radio

   _____

2. ouch I stubbed my toe

   _____

3. wow he pitched a no-hitter

   _____

4. hurrah we won the contest

   _____

5. help I can't find the light switch in the dark

   _____

6. fantastic tickets for the game are still available

   _____

7. sure we will bring sandwiches

   _____

More Punctuation Practice with Interjections

A Add an interjection to each sentence. Be sure to punctuate it correctly.

1. Isn't that car beautiful? _____
2. I won the contest. _____
3. It's hot today. _____
4. I didn't know that. _____
5. I snagged my sweater. _____
6. I dropped the glass. _____
7. Everyone is watching TV. _____
8. I'm late again. _____

B List several more examples of interjections below.

1. _____   4. _____   7. _____

2. _____   5. _____   8. _____

3. _____   6. _____   9. _____

C Use each of the following interjections in a sentence of your own. Punctuate the sentence carefully.

Wow   1. _____

No   2. _____

Quick 3. _____

Ouch   4. _____

Hey   5. _____

Oops   6. _____

Hurry 7. _____

Whew   8. _____

UNIT 1 *MARKS OF END PUNCTUATION* 11

A Find the end of each sentence or interjection in this announcement from a school newspaper. Mark it with a period, question mark, or exclamation point.

Stop Don't turn the page yet

You know our school team is going to the state tournament Wouldn't you like to be there The Alumni Booster Club is making that possible They are arranging for a bus trip to the tournament How much does the trip cost Bus transportation, a two-night stay on the university campus, and all meals cost just $250

Sign up today Space is limited

If you can't make the trip, plan on coming to the school auditorium on Saturday and Sunday The games will be shown on a big-screen television What could be better than watching the game with school friends

Oh Don't forget Friday night is the big pep rally Plan to be there

B On your own paper, rewrite the following paragraphs, adding appropriate marks of end punctuation where needed. Remember, some abbreviations are not acceptable in paragraphs. Write out the whole word for unacceptable abbreviations.

Did you know that Dr and Mrs James R Levitz, Jr, bought the old Reilly house at 438 So Elm St last week What a terrific house It was built for Patrick M Reilly, pres of Reilly Assemblers, Inc, in 1902. The house has stood empty for two years Reilly's granddaughter, Patricia M. Fiore, just sold the house to the Levitzes on Dec 3

When will the Levitzes move in They plan to be in the home by the beginning of Apr Yes It's wonderful It'll be great to have a family living there again

Items in a Series

➤ A comma (,) is a punctuation mark that says "pause." Use a comma to separate items in a series.

We are having fish, salad, and broccoli for dinner.
Every day you should have breakfast, lunch, and dinner.

➤ Use a comma to separate phrases in a series, too.

I bought a puzzle for my father, a book for my mother, and stationery for my sister.
We went to the library, played at the beach, and had a cookout in the park.

Write a sentence using each set of items in a series. Use commas to separate each one.

1. basketball   volleyball   softball

_____

_____

_____

2. petunias   daisies   marigolds

_____

_____

_____

3. stapler   scissors   tape dispenser

_____

_____

_____

4. games   books   toys

_____

_____

_____

U N I T 2

➤ Words that are often used in pairs are set off as one item in a series.

bread and butter   macaroni and cheese
salt and pepper   bed and breakfast

We ate macaroni and cheese, vegetables, bread and butter, and fruit for lunch.

A Separate the items in a series with a comma.

1. Kary Ernesto and Selena work in the same office.

2. My grandmother and grandfather aunt and uncle and cousins visited us last year.

3. We drove through Wyoming Utah and Nevada on our way to California.

4. At the circus, clowns walked on stilts rode unicycles and juggled plates.

5. We had a choice of ham and cheese peanut butter and jelly or turkey sandwiches for lunch.

6. Swimming running and bicycle riding are good forms of exercise.

7. Luis David and Gerardo went horseback riding.

8. The school has soccer track and field and baseball teams.

9. The office equipment included a fax machine a photocopier and several computers.

10. Our city has a number of bed and breakfasts hotels and motels where you can stay.

B Use the following sets of items in sentences. Be sure to punctuate correctly.

1. watched a movie   played games   ate popcorn

_____

_____

_____

2. desk   table and chairs   cabinet

_____

_____

_____

3. in the winter   in the spring   in the fall

_____

_____

_____

Place Names, Dates, and Person's Position

➤ **Place Names:** Commas are used to set off parts of addresses and names of geographical locations and political divisions.

> Please ship the order to Suite 201A, 880 Lee Street, Des Plaines, Illinois 60016, for arrival on Friday.
> The Opera House in Sydney, Australia, is a well-known landmark.

➤ **Dates:** Commas are used to set off the day of the week from a date. In dates, commas are used before and after the year if a specific date is given.

> Jason Moritz began working for this company on Monday, January 14, 1995.
> On January 20, 1992, President Clinton was sworn into office.

Do not place a comma between the month and the year when a specific date is not given.

> The company celebrated its twentieth anniversary in July 1996.

➤ **Person's Position:** A person's title or position is set off by commas when it follows the person's name.

> Maria Torres, former Broadway star, sang at the benefit.
> Daniel Brenner, Ph.D., accepted a position at the university.

A Add commas, if needed, in each of these sentences.

1. That movie opened in New York on Saturday December 9, 1995.

2. The Midwest had record high temperatures in July 1995.

3. Bill Cosby Ed.D. produced and starred in a popular family show in the 1980s.

4. On January 1 2001 a new millennium begins.

5. Write the California Office of Tourism P.O. Box 1499 Sacramento CA 95812 for more information.

B Add commas where necessary in this paragraph.

One of the most popular tourist attractions in Philadelphia Pennsylvania is Independence Hall. In this building, John Hancock president of the Second Continental Congress signed the Declaration of Independence on July 4 1776. It was here that delegates signed the Constitution of the United States on September 17 1787. The hall is located in Independence National Historical Park, which also includes the Liberty Bell Pavilion the Second Bank of the United States Franklin Court and other historical sites. To learn more about the park, write Visitor Center 313 Walnut Avenue Philadelphia PA 19106.

Parenthetical Comments and Adverbs

➤ **Parenthetical Comments:** A parenthetical comment is an aside, an afterthought, or an extra description or saying. Use commas to set off these comments in a sentence to show they are not essential.

> The department manager, harried and tired, was anxious for the store to close.
> Taking a midnight flight, I can assure you, was not my idea.

➤ **Parenthetical Adverbs:** An adverb, such as *also, too, then, however,* and *consequently,* can be used parenthetically. Use commas to set off parenthetical adverbs.

> Sonya caught the ball. Then, she threw it to second base.
> The runner, however, was safe.

A Add commas to set off the parenthetical comments and adverbs in the following sentences.

1. Karl I am quite certain will want to attend the meeting.

2. Rob after all is only in first grade.

3. Consuela of course will be invited to the party.

4. The summer was hot indeed!

5. Sarah on the other hand prefers swimming.

6. Will Kenji run in the marathon too?

7. Now let's try it again.

8. That story as a matter of fact ran on all three news programs.

9. The flight to my surprise left on time.

10. The traffic consequently was backed up for a mile.

B Add commas to these sentences as needed.

1. The coach as a matter of fact is hosting the team's victory celebration on Saturday March 30 1996.

2. By the way did you see the story in the paper this morning?

3. Josh I imagine will enter the 100-meter 500-meter and 1,000-meter races.

4. Erika lives in this neighborhood also.

5. The headquarters of the Sierra Club I believe is in San Francisco California.

Appositives

➤ An appositive is a word or phrase that identifies or explains the noun or pronoun it follows. Separate an appositive from the rest of the sentence with commas.

> Marilu, *my best friend last year,* moved to Tucson, Arizona.
> George Washington, *the first president of the United States,* is called the father of his country.

➤ If the appositive specifies one of two or more people or things, it is not set off by commas. For example, if you had more than one brother, you would NOT use commas.

> My brother Paul was late for dinner. (The appositive *Paul* tells which brother you are referring to. It is not set off by commas.)

➤ If you have only one brother, you would use commas.

> My brother, Paul, was late for dinner. (The appositive tells us your brother's name. It is set off by commas.)

A Underline the appositives in each of the following sentences. Add commas if needed.

1. *Pride and Prejudice* a novel by Jane Austen was adapted as a screenplay for television.

2. Mrs. Menoni the school secretary was absent yesterday.

3. Sandra Day O'Connor Associate Justice of the Supreme Court received her law degree from Stanford University.

4. Have you seen the musical *Evita?*

5. David Kell my next-door neighbor is a police officer.

B Add an appositive, and commas if needed, to each of the following sentences.

1. Felipe _____ had dinner with us last night.

2. Our neighbor _____ is away for the weekend.

3. My favorite actor _____ starred in that movie.

4. Michael Jordan _____ played college ball at the University of North Carolina.

5. Jupiter _____ is over 390 million miles away from Earth.

Nouns of Direct Address

➤ Sometimes you name the person or persons to whom you are speaking. The name is set off by a comma from the rest of the sentence. The name is called a "noun of direct address."

> *Max,* stop yelling.
> Would you come here, *Antonio.*
> My story, *children,* doesn't end there.

➤ The comma may be *before, after,* or *on both sides of* the name.

A Set off the nouns of direct address with commas. Underline the nouns of direct address.

1. Evie would you please wait here.

2. I need your help to perform this act ladies and gentlemen.

3. Are you studying here Terrell or going to the library?

4. Now it is time class to choose a writing topic.

5. Alesandra did you see the president's speech on TV last night?

6. Yes Mr. Perez my report is ready to present to the committee.

7. Listen Claudia and you can hear your heart beat.

8. Do you know what time it is Keagan?

9. I don't believe my friend that I will ever forget you.

10. Akiko is coming with us Michelle.

B Add a noun of direct address to each of the following sentences. Recopy the sentence in the space. Be sure to add commas where they are needed.

1. Yes I'd like another iced tea.

_____

2. Can you give me directions to South Street?

_____

3. I'm sure that we could all use a break.

_____

4. That trail through the park is long and steep.

_____

Commas in a Letter

➤ In a letter, use a comma between the city and the state in an address.
San Francisco, CA

➤ Use a comma between the day and the year in the date.
May 5, 1996

➤ In a friendly letter, use a comma after the greeting.
Dear Rose,

➤ Use a comma after the complimentary close.
Sincerely yours,

A Add commas wherever they are needed in the following letter.

> 228 Second Avenue
> Bellaire TX 77401
> July 17 1996
>
> Dear Jake
>
>   Guess what? We have baseball tickets. That means we'll be able to go to the Astros' game when you and your family are here. It will be great fun! See you soon.
>
>   Your friend
>
>   Estelle

B Punctuate the dates and place names below.

1. February 22 1732

2. April 9 1865

3. May 17 1954

4. January 20 1997

5. Tuesday June 5

6. Pocatello Idaho

7. Buenos Aires Argentina

8. Des Moines Iowa

9. Tucson Arizona

10. Newberry South Carolina

Punctuating Dialogue

➤ Dialogue is conversation. Put quotation marks around the exact words that people say.

➤ Set off a quotation from the rest of the sentence with commas. If the rest of the sentence precedes the quotation, place the comma before the opening quotation mark. If the rest of the sentence follows the quotation, place the comma within the closing quotation mark. If the quotation is a question followed by the rest of the sentence, use a question mark within the closing quotation mark.

> Matthew said, "We have time to play another game before the center closes."
> "Are you sure?" asked Emma.
> "Yes, it's only four o'clock," replied Matthew.

➤ When the rest of the sentence interrupts the quotation, use two commas. Place one comma inside the first closing quotation mark. Place another comma after the interrupting phrase and before the second opening quotation mark.

> "If you stop at the post office," said Sami, "I will mail the package."

A In each sentence, add punctuation to separate the dialogue from the rest of the sentence.

Looking up from the morning paper, Maura asked "Did you see this article about the cave drawings in France?"

"No, what is it about" asked Andrew.

"According to archaeologists" answered Maura "a cave in Chauvet has hundreds of the oldest known cave drawings."

"Really, how old are they" asked Andrew.

Maura replied "The archaeologists think the drawings are between 30,000 and 32,500 years old."

"That is really old" Andrew exclaimed.

"Yes" Maura agreed "it is."

Looking over Maura's shoulder, Andrew noted "I'd like to read that article, too."

"Sure" Maura replied "but I would like it back after you've finished it."

B Write a short dialogue of your own. Punctuate it correctly.

_____

_____

_____

_____

Exclamations

➤ Use a comma to separate a "mild" exclamation from the rest of the sentence. If you use an exclamation point, be sure to capitalize the first word in the sentence. Exclamation points are marks of end punctuation.

     Ah, this water tastes good.
     Ah! This water tastes good!

A Separate the exclamation from the rest of the sentence with a comma or an exclamation point. Be sure the capitalization is correct.

1. No You can't do that!

2. Yes I certainly would like to go to the movies.

3. My this dictionary is heavy.

4. So are you leaving or staying?

5. "Now where exactly are you going?" asked Tara's mother.

B Add an exclamation to each of the following sentences. Add the proper punctuation. Be sure to capitalize the first word of each sentence. Recopy the sentence in the space provided.

1. He did it.

_____

2. The Orioles' Cal Ripken, Jr., broke Lou Gehrig's record.

_____

3. By September 6, 1995, Ripken had played in 2,131 consecutive games.

_____

4. It was thrilling to watch the crowd cheer him.

_____

5. All of Baltimore celebrated his achievement.

_____

UNIT 2

➤ A compound sentence is made up of two or more sentences separated by a comma and joined together with a conjunction.

➤ Some conjunctions that are used to form compound sentences are *and, or, but,* and *for.* Use *but* to join contrasting ideas.
Are you interested in this program, or may I change the channel?
Jack went to the movies, but I stayed home to finish my book.

➤ Three or more short sentences may be punctuated like items in a series.
Leslie got a single, Terry walked, and Karina hit a home run.

■ Combine the following groups of sentences into compound sentences. Add commas and appropriate conjunctions where needed.

1. Ramon likes baseball. John prefers soccer. I like basketball.

_____

_____

2. July was hot. August was hotter. September was glorious.

_____

_____

3. Champ sleeps at the foot of my bed. He sleeps on a throw rug in the kitchen.

_____

_____

4. John Adams was the second president of the United States. His son John Quincy Adams was our sixth president.

_____

_____

5. David skipped breakfast. He was in a hurry.

_____

_____

6. Latitia lost her gloves. She found them in the lost-and-found box at school.

_____

_____

Adverbial Clauses

➤ An introductory adverbial clause appears before the main clause of a sentence. A comma is used to separate an introductory adverbial clause from the rest of the sentence.

> *When Alan reached the front of the line,* the tickets were sold out.
> The tickets were sold out *when Alan reached the front of the line.*

➤ Also, separate an adverbial phrase from the rest of the sentence when it appears before the main clause.

> *Because of the rain,* the tennis match was canceled.
> The tennis match was canceled *because of the rain.*

Underline the adverbial clause or phrase in each sentence. Add a comma after the clause or phrase when it appears at the beginning of the sentence.

1. At the stroke of midnight the crowd greeted the new year.

2. We were leaving the apartment when the phone rang.

3. The president signed the treaty after it was approved by Congress.

4. If you accept the position you will begin work on Monday.

5. Before I get ready to go to work I exercise for twenty minutes.

6. When our poodle sits up and begs no one can resist giving him a treat.

7. Because of its low ratings my favorite TV show was canceled.

8. As long as the lightning streaked through the sky we stayed indoors.

9. Because of a contract dispute the star of the show left the series.

10. We built our cabin at the edge of a silvery woods near a lake.

11. At the edge of a silvery woods near a lake we built a small cabin.

12. By the end of the year the company will be making a profit.

13. After a short intermission the second act of the play began.

14. As she listened to the speaker Cara jotted down questions that she wanted to ask.

15. Just before I started to type my term paper on the computer the electricity went off because of the storm.

U N I T 2

➤ A comma fault occurs when a writer uses a comma instead of end punctuation to separate two sentences. Two sentences separated by a comma is called a "run-on sentence."

➤ Never use a comma to separate two sentences.
  Wrong: We don't have school on Monday, it is Presidents' Day.
  Right: We don't have school on Monday. It is Presidents' Day.

◼ Rewrite each group of words. Find and correct the comma fault.

1. Our baseball team is doing well this year, they hope to win the state championship.

_____

_____

2. Cheryl graduated from high school four years ago, her brother graduated last year.

_____

_____

3. Try to be on time, I don't want to miss the beginning of the movie.

_____

_____

4. What time is the train due, is it late?

_____

_____

5. I'm going to the library, do you want to come with me?

_____

_____

6. Oksana Baiul won the 1994 Olympic gold medal in women's figure skating, she represented Ukraine in the games.

_____

_____

Add commas wherever they are needed in these sentences.

The Birds

Along the ocean shore near Rehoboth Beach Delaware sea gulls are a common sight. They build their nests guard their eggs and rear their young in the grasses near the shore. In the spring Jeri and I went to watch the birds nest. Because we wanted to get a better view we inched our way across the sand toward the grassy part of the beach and there we saw baby gulls small and fluffy huddled in their nests. Suddenly one adult gull flew out of the grasses toward us. Although the gull's movement surprised us we continued to watch the young birds. Then several more gulls making loud warning sounds soared up and flew toward us. When we finally realized what was happening we turned quickly and ran. We fled across the sand to the safety of our car. We opened the doors jumped in the car and slammed the doors shut.

"Whew" I sighed in relief "we're safe!"

Jeri agreed and said "I guess we were too close."

"Yes we certainly were" I replied. "From now on I'm using binoculars to watch the gulls from a distance."

Review Units 1–2

■ In each item, choose the sentence that is correctly punctuated.

_____ 1. We will meet on Tuesday Sept 1
   a. We will meet on Tuesday Sept., 1
   b. We will meet on Tuesday Sept. 1?
   c. We will meet on Tuesday, Sept. 1.
   d. We will meet, on Tuesday Sept. 1.

_____ 2. The birth date of Martin Luther King Jr is celebrated on Jan 15
   a. The birth date, of Martin Luther King, Jr, is celebrated on Jan. 15.
   b. The birth date of Martin Luther King, Jr., is celebrated on Jan. 15.
   c. The birth date of Martin Luther King, Jr, is celebrated on Jan., 15.
   d. The birth date of Martin Luther King, Jr, is celebrated on Jan. 15!

_____ 3. Are the Chicago Cubs the Montreal Expos and the San Diego Padres in baseball's National or American league
   a. Are the Chicago Cubs, the Montreal Expos, and the San Diego Padres in baseball's National or American league?
   b. Are the Chicago Cubs, the Montreal Expos and the San Diego Padres in baseball's National or American league.
   c. Are the Chicago Cubs, the Montreal Expos, and the San Diego Padres in baseball's National or American League.
   d. Are the Chicago Cubs, the Montreal Expos, and the San Diego Padres, in baseball's National or American League.

_____ 4. Actress Ingrid Bergman was born in Stockholm Sweden
   a. Actress, Ingrid Bergman was born in Stockholm, Sweden
   b. Actress, Ingrid Bergman, was born in Stockholm, Sweden,
   c. Actress Ingrid Bergman was born in Stockholm, Sweden.
   d. Actress Ingrid Bergman was born in Stockholm Sweden.

_____ 5. Wow Wasn't the liftoff of *Endeavour* the space shuttle spectacular
   a. Wow! Wasn't the liftoff of *Endeavour* the space shuttle spectacular.
   b. Wow, Wasn't the liftoff of *Endeavour* the space shuttle spectacular?
   c. Wow. Wasn't the liftoff of *Endeavour,* the space shuttle, spectacular
   d. Wow! Wasn't the liftoff of *Endeavour,* the space shuttle, spectacular?

_____ 6. The address is 818 N Cascade Ave Colorado Springs CO 80903.
   a. The address is 818 N. Cascade Ave, Colorado Springs, CO 80903.
   b. The address is 818 N. Cascade Ave. Colorado Springs CO 80903.
   c. The address is 818 N Cascade Ave. Colorado Springs, CO 80903.
   d. The address is 818 N. Cascade Ave., Colorado Springs, CO 80903.

_____ 7. Which award-winning actress is the older sister of Warren Beatty the actor
   a. Which award-winning actress is the older sister of Warren Beatty, the actor?
   b. Which award-winning actress is the older sister of Warren Beatty the actor?
   c. Which award-winning, actress is the older sister of Warren Beatty the actor!
   d. Which award-winning actress is the older sister of Warren Beatty, the actor.

_____ 8. For her book *The Giver* Lois Lowry was awarded the Newberry Medal in 1994
   a. For her book, *The Giver,* Lois Lowry was awarded the Newbery Medal, in 1994,
   b. For her book *The Giver,* Lois Lowry was awarded the Newbery Medal in 1994.
   c. For her book *The Giver* Lois Lowry was awarded the Newbery Medal in 1994
   d. For her book *The Giver* Lois Lowry was awarded the Newbery Medal in 1994!

Semicolons

➤ A semicolon (;) is "halfway" between a period and a comma. It represents a longer pause than a comma but a shorter pause than a period.

Rule One: Use a semicolon to join two related sentences when you do not use a conjunction.

Rule Two: Use a comma to join main clauses with the conjunctions *and, but, or, nor, for,* and *yet.*

It's Your Choice

Usually, in these situations, you may also choose to use a period and start a new sentence. If the sentences are short, they will be "choppy."

Right: Janet is the team's center, and Georgeanne is a forward. (comma plus the conjunction)

Right: Janet is the team's center; Georgeanne is a forward. (semicolon)

Right: Janet is the team's center. Georgeanne is a forward. (period)

Read the items carefully. Find the places where punctuation is needed. Add a comma and a conjunction or a semicolon.

1. Aerobic dancing is good exercise it is also fun.

2. Matt and Ellen go to an Irish step class once a week they learn traditional dances at the class.

3. They enjoy the classes they practice the dances at home, too.

4. On weekends, Matt and Ellen meet with friends at the social club there they dance to an Irish band.

5. Matt never seems to get tired he says that he could dance all night.

6. They enjoy the music of the Irish Rovers the band plays at the club every weekend.

7. The band is made up of local men and women they have been playing together for five years.

8. They have played in the St. Patrick's Day parade they also play at weddings.

Joining Main Clauses with Semicolons

Rule Three: Use a semicolon between main clauses joined by conjunctive adverbs and adverbial phrases.

Conjunctive Adverbs and Adverbial Phrases		
accordingly	nevertheless	consequently
however	on the other hand	for example
then	therefore	thus
in addition	meanwhile	furthermore
that is	still	moreover

➤ You may also put a comma after the conjunctive adverb or adverbial phrase.

> The entire class posed for the picture; however, three students were absent.

Read the sentences carefully. Find the places where semicolons are needed. You may also add commas after the conjunctive adverbs or adverbial phrases.

1. It is early November still a heavy snowstorm is falling.

2. Janice had to hurry otherwise she would miss the bus.

3. The quarterback faked a pass then he ran for a first down.

4. August was unusually cool on the other hand record high temperatures were reported in July.

5. A tornado had been sighted therefore the weather bureau issued a tornado warning.

6. Remember to turn your clocks back one hour in addition replace the batteries in your smoke detectors.

7. The Jacksons are saving to buy a house meanwhile they are living in an apartment.

8. As office manager, Sara has many responsibilities for example she prepares the work schedule and assigns projects.

9. My appointment was for 10:00 however it was rescheduled.

10. We were caught in traffic consequently we missed the first few minutes of the movie.

Semicolons with Conjunctions

Rule Four: Usually, you use a comma before conjunctions. If there are commas within the clauses, use a semicolon between main clauses even if they are connected by *conjunctions.*

> Juan, M. J., and Suzanne are friends; but they do not go to the same school.
> (Use a semicolon to connect the clauses.)

> Juan and Suzanne are friends, but they do not go to the same school.
> (Use a comma only.)

> I like coffee, tea, and soda; but Cory, my friend from work, drinks only water and fruit juice.
> (Use a semicolon to connect the clauses.)

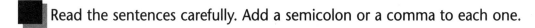 Read the sentences carefully. Add a semicolon or a comma to each one.

1. The storm had raged for hours and the weather bureau advised people to stay home.

2. Ice, snow, and sleet made the roads treacherous but Ron made it to work safely.

3. This was his day off but all paramedics, including Ron, had been asked to report to work.

4. Ron and the other paramedics were kept busy all day for there were many emergencies in town.

5. In just six hours, Ron, Angie, and Tomas made 11 calls and they were all exhausted.

6. They were tired but they were pleased that they were able to help so many people.

Colons and Items in a Series

➤ A colon (:) is a mark that says to the reader, "Pay attention. Something important is coming."

Rule Five: Use a colon before a list of items. Do not use a colon if the list follows a verb or a preposition.

> Pat has three children: Ed, Zachary, and Melissa.
> Pat's three children are Ed, Zachary, and Melissa.

> We eat these cereals for breakfast: shredded wheat, oatmeal, and cream of wheat.
> For breakfast, we eat shredded wheat, oatmeal, or cream of wheat.

Read the sentences carefully. Add a colon before each list of items if needed. Separate each item in the series with a comma.

1. These actors starred in the classic movie *The Wizard of Oz* Judy Garland as Dorothy Burt Lahr as the Cowardly Lion Jack Haley as the Tin Man and Ray Bolger as the Scarecrow.

2. My favorite books are *The Client The Color Purple* and *To Dance with the White Dog.*

3. Patty bought all the items on her shopping list carrots milk eggs paper napkins and cornflakes.

4. Corinne planted three kinds of flowers in her garden zinnias marigolds and petunias.

5. We could use the following tools during the math test calculator protractor ruler and compass.

6. The lunch menu included these choices salad pasta in sauce turkey and potatoes green beans milk or juice and fruit.

7. The House of Representatives has only one member from each of these states Alaska Delaware Montana North Dakota South Dakota Vermont and Wyoming.

8. On her European trip, Marie visited Germany Italy Switzerland and France.

Germany

Switzerland

France

Italy

Semicolons and Items in a Series

Rule Six: A comma is usually used to separate items in a series. If the items have commas, however, use a semicolon.

➤ Don't forget the colon when it's needed!

Several people presented papers at the conference: Kathy Smith, a teacher from Philadelphia; Arnold Douglas, a writer from Milwaukee; and Roland Quaker, a retired merchant from Salem, Oregon.

Read the sentences carefully. Add a colon where it is needed. Then add semicolons or commas to separate items in the lists.

1. The following people were responsible for this video Pat Bollino, producer Dave Scheidhauer, director and Michael Josephowitz, camera operator.

2. The reading list included these titles *A Tale of Two Cities Jane Eyre* and *The House of the Seven Gables.*

3. My summer garden has splendid vegetables tomatoes lettuce green peppers radishes and onions.

4. Class members took these parts in the moot court trial the judge defense attorney and defendant the prosecutor witnesses and jury.

5. A number of relatives from out of town attended my wedding Aunt Jennifer and Uncle Bill from San Diego, California Cousin Norma from Juneau, Alaska and Uncle Robert from Erie, Pennsylvania.

6. Jill's cinema class viewed these classic films *Citizen Kane Casablanca* and *It Happened One Night.*

7. Michiko's wish list included computer games CDs by Whitney Houston, Wynona Judd, and Garth Brooks and clothes.

8. Caroline's table was covered with vegetables for soup zucchini celery carrots beans and onions.

9. I signed up for three evening classes computer programming beginning Spanish and American history.

10. Among the people who received the Presidential Medal of Freedom, the highest civilian award in the United States, were General Colin Powell, military officer Thurgood Marshall, public servant Arthur Ashe, athlete and Martha Ray, entertainer.

UNIT 3

1. A colon is used in the formal salutation in a letter.
   Dear Mayor Sindles:

2. A colon is used to separate the hour from the minutes
   in figures of clock time.
   10:10 A.M.   12:45 P.M.

3. A colon is used to separate a title and its subtitle and
   a chapter number and title.
   The Time of Our Lives: The Early Years
   Chapter 10: "Keeping Records on Your Home Computer"

 Add colons and semicolons as needed in the following letter.

February 10, 1996

Mr. Peter Lawson
Telephonics Corporation
227 Western Avenue
Highwood, Illinois 60040

Dear Mr. Lawson

Thank you for the opportunity to discuss the position available in your
company. As I explained during our phone conversation, I have
completed my courses for my degree however, I am still working on my
master's thesis. I look forward to the interview at 1015 A.M. on Tuesday,
February 20.

Enclosed with this letter, please find the following my résumé letters of
reference from several of my college professors, my former employer,
and the hospital's director of volunteers and the sample reports you
requested. I am looking forward to meeting you I have heard a lot about
your company.

By the way, I read your book, *Telecommunications The Past and Future.* I
found Chapter 9 "The New Age of Telecommunications" particularly
interesting.

Sincerely yours,

Iyo Miura

> **Before You Start**
> Read the following sentences out loud so that you can "hear" the differences
> among the pauses for a comma, a period, and a semicolon.

Mac lives in Minnesota, and Sue lives in Maine.   (comma: short pause)
Mac lives in Minnesota. Sue lives in Maine.   (period: long pause)
Mac lives in Minnesota; however, Sue lives in Maine.   (semicolon and comma: two pauses)

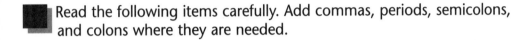 Read the following items carefully. Add commas, periods, semicolons, and colons where they are needed.

1. During December, January, and February, the Hendersons live in Florida but their main home is in New Hampshire.

2. The Venturas live in Burlington, Vermont their daughter and grandchildren live in Provo, Utah.

3. Rita visited her sister in Houston for a month then she returned to Denver.

4. Dana planned to watch the game Tom rented a video and Daria, Jeff, and Erin went to the park.

5. Mike and Elena's son is in college however their daughter is still in high school.

6. I read *Moon Mother A Native American Creation Tale* to my second-grade class.

7. We had a choice of three entrees broiled white fish, chicken Kiev, and roast beef.

8. Dear Ms. Sagan
   Thank you for your excellent presentation the entire staff enjoyed listening to your ideas.

9. Jude said that dinner would be served at 730 P.M. sharp.

10. Architect Frank Lloyd Wright designed and built these houses the Willets House in Highland Park, Illinois the Robie House in Chicago and the Kaufmann House near Uniontown, Pennsylvania.

Apostrophes and Contractions

➤ A contraction is a shortened word form. Use an apostrophe to indicate the missing letter or letters.

do not   *don't*   should not   *shouldn't*   I will   *I'll*

A Supply the missing letters. Write out each contraction. Use a dictionary if necessary.

Example: wouldn't   ___would not___

1. didn't   _____   6. can't   _____

2. isn't   _____   7. I'd   _____

3. we'll   _____   8. you've   _____

4. don't   _____   9. shouldn't   _____

5. it's   _____   10. they're   _____

B Write the boldface words in the form of a contraction.

Example: ___It's___   **It is** really cold out there today!
    ___won't___   Carla **will not** give her brother any ice cream.

_____   1. Sidney **has not** applied for that position.

_____   2. **Do not** open that door!

_____   3. Anthony said that **he would** drive next week.

_____   4. Rita **would not** be late without a good reason.

_____   5. **They will** call after they reach the hotel.

_____   6. I **can not** be there until 10:00 A.M.

_____   7. **Who is** coming with me?

_____   8. Oren **did not** miss a single day of school last year.

_____   9. **You will** want to take a warm jacket.

_____   10. **I have** two tickets for the game.

Plurals

➤ Use an apostrophe and -s to form the plurals of numerals and letters.
> Linda always forgets to dot her i's.
> Larry gets his 9's and his 6's confused.

➤ Some writers do not use an apostrophe when the meaning is clearly understood.
> Sheila got two Bs on her report card.
> The Great Depression took place in the 1930s.

A Write a sentence for each of the following plurals.

7's   **1.** _____

A's   **2.** _____

t's   **3.** _____

Also use an apostrophe to show that numbers are missing from years.
> The title of the program was "Growth through the '90s."
> My parents grew up in the early '60s.

B Add apostrophes wherever they are needed in the following sentences.

When I was a very young girl in the 80s, I spent part of my summer

visiting my grandparents. Whenever we went somewhere, Grandma would

say, "Now mind your ps and qs." I didnt know what Grandma meant by

that phrase. It wasnt until much later that I learned my grandmother was

telling me to behave myself.

A Special Case
Sometimes an apostrophe in a contraction takes the place of letters and words.
For example, the contraction *o'clock* stands for the words *of the clock.*

Rules for Possessives

➤ A possessive noun can be singular or plural.

Rule 1: Make a singular noun possessive by adding an apostrophe and *-s*.

Singular	Singular Possessive
man	man's watch
Sharon	Sharon's role

Rule 2: Make a plural noun that ends in *s* possessive by adding an apostrophe.

Plural	Plural Possessive
bears	bears' den
trucks	trucks' cargo

Rule 3: Make a plural noun that does not end in *s* possessive by adding an apostrophe and *-s*.

Plural	Plural Possessive
sheep	sheep's pasture
women	women's basketball conference

Underline the possessive noun in each sentence. Write *Singular* or *Plural* in the space. Two examples are done for you.

Singular   Jack's car is parked on the corner.

Plural   Both of my brothers' wives are attorneys.

_____ 1. The children's room is down the hall.

_____ 2. Tom's books were scattered across his desk.

_____ 3. The students' artwork decorated the classroom.

_____ 4. She belongs to the professional women's caucus.

_____ 5. Dad's lasagna is great!

_____ 6. The teachers' meeting began at four o'clock.

_____ 7. The car's radiator overheated.

_____ 8. The school's curriculum included classes in sign language.

_____ 9. The president's speech was televised live.

_____ 10. The trees' branches were bent by snow.

Singular Possessives

➤ Use an apostrophe and an -s to form a possessive noun. A possessive noun shows ownership or a relationship.

Ownership: That book belongs to Alicia.
That book is *Alicia's.*
Alicia's book is here.

Relationship: Maria is the sister of Carlos.
Maria is *Carlos's sister.*

A Rewrite each of the singular nouns below so that it is possessive. You will need to add something for the noun to possess. Study the examples carefully.

Examples: book   *The book's cover*   Jackie *Jackie's sister*

1. computer   _____

2. person   _____

3. animal   _____

4. Catherine   _____

5. flower   _____

B Find the possessive nouns in the sentences below. Rewrite the word and add an apostrophe.

Jack Horner, a paleontologist, helped change the scientific communitys

ideas about dinosaurs. The paleontologists crew searched Montanas western

region for dinosaur fossils. There the team found duck-billed dinosaur fossils,

including nests, eggs, and newly hatched young. Horners teams discoveries

provided evidence about the habits of duck-billed dinosaurs. Clues led the team

to believe that the dinosaurs returned to nest at the same site year after year.

The region of Horners dig sites is now called Egg Mountain.

Plural Possessives

➤ Most plural nouns end in *-s* or *-es.* A plural noun that is possessive ends in *-s* plus an apostrophe.

Plural Noun	**Plural Possessive**
baskets	baskets' contents
friends	friends' help

A Rewrite each of the following plural nouns so that it is possessive. You will need to add something for the noun to possess. Study the examples carefully.

Examples: buildings   the buildings' structure
players   the players' victory

athletes 1. _____

stories   2. _____

rivers   3. _____

turkeys   4. _____

workers   5. _____

B Read each of the following sentences. Decide whether the boldfaced word is plural or possessive. Write the answer in the space.

Examples: *possessive* Tom makes the **world's** best barbecue sauce.

plural   Henry's library **books** are overdue.

_____ 1. Jesse is the drummer in his **brother's** band.

_____ 2. Her **classmates** tried out for the school play.

_____ 3. The **doctor's** orders were for bed rest.

_____ 4. We heard the **dog's** howls all night.

_____ 5. The **park's** summer program began this week.

_____ 6. Melissa invited four **friends** to her slumber party.

_____ 7. One of **Ecuador's** most important crops is bananas.

_____ 8. Although they cannot fly, **emus** are fast runners.

_____ 9. Caracas is **Venezuela's** capital.

_____ 10. The **cabin's** fireplace is made of stone.

Apostrophes in Phrases

➤ Use an apostrophe in phrases such as "a moment's rest" or "five minutes' work."

Singular Possessive Nouns
one dollar's worth
a week's vacation

Plural Possessive Nouns
two dollars' worth
two weeks' vacation

➤ Use apostrophes to form possessives with indefinite pronouns.
   Everyone's ideas were considered.

Read each sentence carefully. Correct any errors. Recopy the sentence in the space provided.

1. Mike's job entitles him to one weeks' vacation.

_____

2. I need four dollar's worth of quarters.

_____

3. The library is an hours' walk from here.

_____

4. She wanted to rest at the days end.

_____

5. "I just need a moments notice to be ready," Mr. Gerald said.

_____

6. "Could I have a dollars worth of change, please?"

_____

7. We usually shop for a weeks worth of food at a time.

_____

8. When Ann will be here is anyones' guess.

_____

9. Someones jacket was still hanging in the closet.

_____

10. We think that everyones ideas are important.

_____

A Add apostrophes where they are needed in the sentences. Write the sentences correctly in the space provided.

1. Katherines report wasnt due for a week.

_____

2. The stores special of the month was blueberry frozen yogurt.

_____

3. The "oldies" radio station plays hits from the 60s, 70s, and 80s.

_____

4. Ill need more than a moments notice to get ready.

_____

5. I reminded my second graders to cross their ts.

_____

6. "Everyones ticket is in the envelope," Ms. Jones explained.

_____

B Identify the word in bold in each of the sentences below as either a plural or a plural possessive. Add an apostrophe if necessary.

   plural   The **seals** jumped through the rings at the aquarium show.

   plural possessive   "**Men's** clothes are over there," said the salesperson.

_____   1. These two **families** live in the same apartment building.

_____   2. The **boys** father went with them to the soccer game.

_____   3. The **twins** favorite author is Beverly Cleary.

_____   4. The **girls** gymnastics team is in the state tournament.

_____   5. The **stores** do not open until 11:00 A.M.

_____   6. The **geeses** flight pattern is V-shaped.

Direct Quotations

➤ A quotation includes the exact words that someone says. Use quotation marks ("/") to set off all direct quotations.

"I answered all those questions correctly," said Rafael.

Kate asked, "Who can give me a ride to the mall?"

A Supply the missing quotation marks in the following sentences.

1. Are you going to the dance tonight? Jeremy asked Rowena.

2. Yes, I am, answered Rowena. It's going to be fun. Everyone is going to be there.

3. Everyone except me, sighed Jeremy.

4. Why aren't you going? Rowena asked.

5. Jeremy replied, I have to work tonight.

6. That's too bad, said Rowena.

Use quotation marks before and after the exact words that someone says.

"Yes," said Sam, "I do plan to be at the party."

B Add quotation marks to the sentences below.

1. There is a rich cultural heritage, the narrator said, in the villages of West Africa.

2. I would love to visit there, Alex said. Perhaps I shall someday.

3. Let's go to the African art display at the museum, suggested Emilio.

4. That would be a good place to begin our study, replied Alex.

5. I can go there tomorrow, said Emilio. How about you, Alex?

6. Tomorrow would be fine with me, answered Alex. Let's meet at 3 P.M.

Indirect Quotations

➤ Do not put quotation marks around indirect quotations.

Indirect Quotation: Mike said that he would be late.
Direct Quotation: Mike said, "I will be late."

A Add quotation marks to the following sentences as needed.

1. Janet said that fall was her favorite time of year.

2. I agree, said Gilberto. The trees all look so beautiful.

3. I love the crisp, cool weather, continued Janet.

4. Gilberto suggested that today would be a good day to go on a hike.

5. Janet thought that was an excellent idea. OK, she said, let's go.

B Identify each sentence as a direct or an indirect quotation. Add quotation marks where they are needed.

Indirect	Janet asked her mother for some help.
7 Direct	"Could you help me?" Janet asked her mother.
_____	1. Is everyone asleep? Harold asked softly.
_____	2. We were wondering where everyone was.
_____	3. Where is everyone? I wondered out loud.
_____	4. Perhaps they are asleep, my friend replied.
_____	5. Just then everyone yelled, Surprise!
_____	6. They shouted that they had fooled us.
_____	7. Were you really surprised? asked Colleen.
_____	8. We certainly were, gasped Harold.
_____	9. Everyone said they were glad that the surprise party had worked.
_____	10. Let's do this again next year, laughed Harold.
_____	11. I'll be there, said Colleen.
_____	12. Harold said that he'd put it on his calendar.

Quote within a Quote

➤ Use single quotation marks ('/') to enclose a quotation within a quotation.
   John said, "And then my mother asked, 'At what time is your interview?'"

■ Read the following sentences carefully. Add commas, quotation marks, and single quotation marks where they are needed.

1. Tomorrow and tomorrow creeps this petty pace is a line from Shakespeare's *Macbeth* said Mr. Donellan, my English teacher.

2. What short story begins with the line Nervous, you say I'm nervous? asked Ms. Riccardi.

3. After school be sure to stop by the library suggested the teacher. Your research reports are due next week.

4. Skimming an asphalt sea are words from my brother's favorite poem about skateboarding said Toni.

5. Tica said, I heard Sandy yell, Watch out for my cat! as the car came speeding down the street.

6. Julio said to me, Don't tell anyone about the secret passage whispered Sue.

7. Larry called, Andrea, Mom said Answer the front door.

8. Mrs. Jones said, This book says that Paul Bunyan put trees into his pockets.

9. Kelly told me with great certainty, I don't want to go there, and so I won't! Pat said to his mother.

10. What is meant by the poetry line Miles to go before I sleep? asked William.

11. The nutrition book says Eat raw vegetables at least once a day read Marta.

12. To sleep, perchance to dream is my favorite line from *Hamlet* said Shane.

Titles

➤ Use quotation marks around titles of short literary and musical works.

Short stories:	"To Build a Fire" by Jack London
Poems:	"Birches" by Robert Frost
Magazine or newspaper articles:	"Exercise for Health"
Titles of chapters:	Chapter 3: "My Trip to West Africa"
Songs:	"Sounds of Silence" by Simon and Garfunkel

A Add quotation marks around the titles in these sentences.

1. Throwing a Fast Ball is a short story written by pitcher Jim Palmer.

2. Maggie enjoyed reading The Raven, a poem by Edgar Allan Poe.

3. The chorus is singing Climb Every Mountain as their final number.

4. Your assignment is to read Chapter 12: First Years under the Presidents.

5. The magazine's cover story about junk mail was titled Read This!

B Place quotation marks around the titles in these sentences.

1. I quoted lines from The Desert Sea, an article about the Red Sea, in my report.

2. This anthology includes the short story A Rose for Emily.

3. Mother to Son is one of my favorite poems by Langston Hughes.

4. In 1993, Whitney Houston won a Grammy Award for her recording of I Will Always Love You.

5. An excellent, but sad, short story is The Wall by Albert Camus.

6. Chapter 3 in the book is titled Shortcuts.

Other Kinds of Titles
Titles of books, magazines, operas, and plays are printed in italics. When you write by hand, you should underline these titles.

Proofreading Practice

A Read the following dialogue. Add quotation marks where they are needed.

Allen walked into the studio. Where are the new microphones we ordered? he asked.

In the corner cabinet, said Mitchell.

Oh, I found them, said Allen.

Mitchell asked Allen why he needed the microphones.

The band is playing tonight, and we need the extra mikes, Allen replied.

Where is the band playing? Mitchell asked.

At the teen club's dance. Come by later if you can, said Allen.

Thanks, I'll try to make it, Mitchell said as Allen rushed out the door.

B Read the following sentences. Add regular and single quotation marks only where they are needed.

1. I remember Ms. Sorvino said, Do the problems on pages 26 and 27 for homework, Jane said.

2. Are you sure those are the pages that we're supposed to do? asked Susan.

3. Jane told her that Theo had written down the same page numbers.

4. I think I'll call Mai to make sure, as my mother always says Better to be safe than sorry, said Susan.

5. Well, I'm absolutely sure, Jane said again. Absolutely sure.

6. After talking to Mai, Susan agreed that they were to do the first two pages of Chapter 2: Simple Equations.

7. Jane said, Let's get started. I also have to read The Furnished Room, a short story by O. Henry, for English class.

8. Right, I have other homework, too, Susan said.

Review Units 3–5

Rewrite each sentence, adding appropriate punctuation where needed.

1. Like many other insects, beetles have four stages of life egg, larva, pupa, and adult.

2. Phoenix, Arizonas capital, is the states largest city.

3. In Shakespeares play Julius Caesar, the last words spoken by Caesar are Et tu, Brute?

4. Have you read At Annikas Place or any other poems by Siv Widerberg? Charlotte asked.

5. Tami answered, The earth has seven continents Asia is the largest continent Australia is the smallest.

6. George always says that hed rather drive than fly when traveling on business.

7. The restaurant listed the chefs dinner specials tortelacci with clam, tomato, or meat sauce lemon chicken with choice of baked potato, scalloped potatoes, or wild rice and broiled fish with vegetables.

8. O. Henrys short story The Gift of the Magi has a surprise ending.

9. Bill Haley and the Comets recorded their hit song Rock around the Clock during the 50s.

10. A French soldier in Napoleons army in Egypt found the Rosetta Stone in 1799 it provided the key for decoding Egyptian hieroglyphics.

The Dash

➤ A dash is a line used to mark a break in thought. You can use a long line (—)
to show the change in thought. Some sentences require two dashes.
"Is it—I mean, is this really Michael Jordan's autograph?"
He said—you heard him—that he'd be happy to help.

A Rewrite the following sentences, adding dashes where needed.

1. Are you are you really moving?

2. I bought I mean, I am going to buy a new car.

3. Walk west make that east to the corner of Fifth and Bloom Streets.

4. Next, the recipe calls for let me see two cups of flour.

5. Hand me the pliers no, the wrench so that I can tighten this pipe.

In an informal situation you can use a dash instead of a colon to introduce a list.
Yes, I'd like something to drink—milk, water, lemonade, anything.

B Add dashes to the following sentences where they are needed.

Do you want to come with me I think you'd have fun to the park? I'm

going to bring my baseball gear bat, ball, and glove. Maybe we can find

enough people for a basketball game I mean, baseball game. I know at

least I think Randi and Mark will be there. I'm leaving soon in about a half

hour if you want to come.

More Uses of Dashes

➤ Use dashes to set off a sudden parenthetical phrase.
   A look of surprise—or was it fear?—came over her face as she stepped through the door.

➤ Also use dashes to set off a parenthetical phrase that has commas within it.
   The baby crawled—enthusiastically, yet cautiously—toward me.

Rewrite the sentences below. Add dashes where they are needed.

1. She could have and indeed, should have checked all the options.

   _____

2. The umpire decided quickly, yet with certainty that the runner was out.

   _____

3. Celia typed her report thorough and well researched over the weekend.

   _____

4. Seeing the barrier and sign closed for repairs Jamal drove to the next exit.

   _____

5. The poem short, yet meaningful tells about choices.

   _____

Also, you may use the dash before a credit line giving the author's name after a quotation. In this situation, quotation marks are not needed.

   We must all hang together, or assuredly, we shall all hang separately.
      —Benjamin Franklin,
         to the others at the signing of the Declaration of Independence.

   Justice is truth in action. —Benjamin Disraeli.

Ellipses

➤ An ellipsis is three dots (...). Use ellipses (plural) to mark missing words within a quotation. An ellipsis can show that the last words of a quotation or entire paragraphs are missing.

➤ Use an ellipsis when you want to include only the highlights or important points from a lengthy passage. However, you want the reader to know that you have left out some of the author's words. Sometimes you leave out a part of a sentence, and yet the remaining portion of the sentence is a complete thought. You then leave the sentence's end punctuation and add the three dots after the end punctuation.

> I'm an archaeologist, and ... I lived with a human once, and I know it isn't as simple as they told us back in school. (Remaining portion of the sentence is not a complete thought.)

> I'm an archaeologist, and humans are my business.... I lived with a human once, and I know it isn't as simple as they told us back in school. (Remaining portion of the sentence is a complete thought.)

> —Alan Block from "Humans Are Different"

Rewrite the following paragraph. Eliminate unnecessary sentences. Use an ellipsis to indicate that parts have been left out. Be sure your paragraph still makes sense.

> To function properly, your face needs to be washed carefully every day—preferably at least twice a day. A good cleansing program is important as it serves several purposes. Washing your face removes dirt. Also, it takes away dead cells that would otherwise remain on the surface of the skin. Dead cells spoil your skin's appearance and prevent it from breathing. Finally, a good cleansing also softens the skin. Remember these facts and take care of your skin!

_____

_____

_____

_____

_____

_____

Note: Use ellipses only to leave out nonessential parts of quoted material. Be sure you do not change the author's meaning.

Proofreading Practice

A Rewrite the sentences below. Add dashes where they are needed.

1. Mary looked at Rob happy, excited as he told her the good news.

2. Is it could it be a true story?

3. Catalina's strengths patience, courage, consideration of others, and compassion helped make her a good counselor.

B Rewrite the following paragraph to take out words, phrases, and/or sentences. Use ellipses to show where words have been left out. Be sure your new paragraph makes sense.

There are two kinds of scallops—bay and sea. Bay scallops are smaller, sweeter, and more tender. They take less time to cook but cost considerably more than their ocean-dwelling relatives. Both varieties are tough and dry if cooked too long or at a temperature that is too high.

Prefixes and the Hyphen

➤ Use a hyphen to join prefixes and proper nouns or adjectives and to join prefixes to numerals or time periods.

un-American activities   mid-July
pre-1960s   post-eighteenth century

A Read the following sentences. Add hyphens where they are needed.

1. I went to college in the mid 1980s.

2. The protesters carried signs with anti American slogans.

3. In 1962 the Trans Canada Highway was officially opened.

4. Language classes were held for non English speakers.

5. The supermarket had a post Thanksgiving sale on turkey.

➤ Also use a hyphen to join these prefixes with a word: *self-, ex-,* and *all-.*

self-imposed   self-defense
ex-president   ex-governor
all-American   all-star

B Read the sentences below. Add hyphens where they are needed.

1. Alicia is taking a class in self defense.

2. Joan Turner is self employed.

3. By mid November I had applied to four universities.

4. Ex President Bush spoke to the reporters.

5. This is a good example of pre Columbian art.

6. Vincent won the all state championship in wrestling.

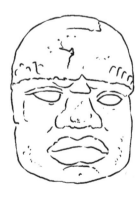

UNIT 7 *HYPHENS*   51

Compound Words

➤ Use a hyphen to form compound words ending with -in-law
  mother-in-law   brother-in-law

A Read the sentences below. Add hyphens where they are needed.

1. "Have you met my father in law?" asked June.

2. My sister in law lives in New Mexico.

3. Janet's brother in law is my son's history teacher.

4. Florence provides nursing care for her mother in law.

5. Ty was the campaign manager for his sister in law.

Use a hyphen to join two or more words that act as an adjective before a noun.
  fine-feathered friends   spur-of-the-moment decision

B Insert hyphens where they are needed in these sentences.

1. My father opened an interest bearing checking account.

2. This is an up to date atlas.

3. The engineers are trying to develop a fuel efficient engine.

4. We want to avoid any last minute changes in our travel arrangements.

5. My brother in law is taking a computer course.

6. Evelyn moved into a five story apartment building.

7. The lightning struck tree crashed to the ground.

8. We plan to replace this well worn carpet in the spring.

9. Only one person could be seen walking down the rain washed street.

10. Rinaldo has a two year old car.

More Compound Words

➤ Use a hyphen to form compound words such as *V-neck* and *T-shirt*.
   The softball team wore matching T-shirts.
   Do you like V-neck sweaters?

A Read the sentences below. Add hyphens where they are needed.

1. Diane wore a V neck sweater with her jeans.

2. Steven wore a tie-dyed T shirt to school.

3. You cannot make a U turn on this street.

4. My younger sister plays T ball in the children's baseball program.

5. The Wilmots built an A frame cabin near the river.

6. The geese flew in a V shaped pattern.

7. The carpenter used a C clamp to hold the wood together until the glue dried.

8. The local theater owner refuses to show G rated movies.

B Circle words that should be hyphenated in these sentences. Write them correctly.

father-in-law

Example: My (father in law) is planning to retire next year.

1. Light colored clothing helps reflect heat on a hot day.

2. Abdul has a twenty year old brother.

3. The S curve in the road is particularly hazardous when the street is wet.

4. Everyone says that ours is a fast moving society.

5. Gabriella bought day old bread for dressing.

6. Ed lifted the fifty pound weight.

7. The Smolicks have a U shaped driveway.

8. The Boeing 747 is a wide bodied jet.

➤ Use a hyphen to form compound numbers from *twenty-one* to *ninety-nine.*

twenty-one   seventy-nine   thirty-eight

A Add hyphens where they are needed in the following sentences.

1. February has twenty eight days except during leap year when it has twenty nine.

2. March and July have thirty one days every year.

3. Mariana will be forty two on May 1.

4. "Seventy Six Trombones" is a song from the musical *The Music Man.*

5. The House of Representatives has thirty one members from New York.

6. A piano has eighty eight keys—thirty six black keys and fifty two white ones.

7. The children collected ninety one dollars in pennies.

8. Two dozen equals twenty four.

Use a hyphen in fractions unless the numerator or denominator has a hyphenated number.

one-half cup   seven thirty-seconds of an inch
two-thirds of the vote   five and seven-tenths of a meter

B Add hyphens where they are needed in the following sentences.

1. Eleven twenty seconds is equal to one half.

2. An amendment must be ratified by three quarters of the states to become part of the Constitution.

3. About two fifths of Africa is covered by desert.

4. The class spent one half of the period discussing current events.

5. The recipe called for one quarter cup of butter or margarine.

6. One third of the council voted against the new ordinance.

7. The ordinance passed by a two thirds majority.

8. Use five sixths water and one sixth detergent for the cleaning solution.

9. The school is one and four fifths miles away from my apartment building.

10. We waited in line for one and one half hours to buy concert tickets.

Proofreading Practice

A Add hyphens to the following words. Use each word in a sentence, adding hyphens if necessary.

sister in law   **1.** _____

_____

G rated   **2.** _____

_____

all star   **3.** _____

_____

ex senator   **4.** _____

_____

time honored   **5.** _____

_____

twenty one   **6.** _____

_____

mid 1900s   **7.** _____

_____

two thirds   **8.** _____

_____

B Add hyphens in the following sentences.

Jeanne Boudine was only twenty seven years old when she decided to start her own clothing design business. Before becoming a self employed designer, she sought advice on how to finance her dream. She talked with her father in law, an ex president of the First National Bank. He told her to apply for short term bank loans.

That was five and one half years ago. Now Jeanne is a well known sportswear designer. Her T shirts, sweatpants, and exercise clothes are sold throughout the country. She has even designed uniforms for the all star basketball team. Today, we are here to honor Jeanne as mid America's entrepreneur of the year.

Division between Syllables

➤ Sometimes you run out of space at the end of a line when your are writing. You may have to divide a word at the end of the line. You cannot divide the word just anywhere. You must divide it between syllables. Use a hyphen to indicate that the word continues on the next line. Always check a dictionary if you have any doubts about where to divide a word into syllables.

Every syllable must have a vowel.

The vowels are *a, e, i, o, u,* and sometimes *y.*

Rule One: When two consonants come between vowels, divide between the consonants if they are pronounced separately.

basket	bas-ket	(*s* and *k* are pronounced separately.
captain	cap-tain	(*p* and *t* are pronounced separately.)

Rule Two: If the two unlike consonants are not pronounced separately, divide before or after the consonants.

clothing	cloth-ing	(*th* are pronounced together)
zebras	ze-bras	(*br* are pronounced together)

▪ Divide each word according to one of the rules above. Use the dictionary if you are not sure.

1. forward _____

2. master _____

3. certain _____

4. feathers _____

5. buckets _____

6. mustard _____

7. pardon _____

8. gathers _____

9. whisper _____

10. barter _____

11. fiction _____

12. rockets _____

Double Consonants

➤ Usually, divide words between double consonants.

    tunnel   tun-nel

    manner   man-ner

A Divide each word according to the rule above. Use the dictionary if you are not sure.

1. coffee   _____

2. matter   _____

3. carrot   _____

4. shopper _____

5. hammer _____

6. willow   _____

7. rotten   _____

8. letter   _____

➤ Ordinarily, divide between parts of compound words.

    windmill   wind-mill

    softball   soft-ball

B Divide each word according to the rule above. Use the dictionary if you are not sure.

Example: blackout   *black-out*

1. seashell   _____

2. dustpan   _____

3. tugboat   _____

4. outside   _____

5. handmade _____

6. heartfelt _____

7. spotlight _____

8. newspaper _____

Some Important Don'ts

1. Don't divide a one-syllable word.
   peace   short

2. Don't divide a word so that one letter stands alone at the end of one line or at the beginning of the next. Avoid dividing a word so that two letters stand alone on a line.
   ahead   helper

3. Don't divide a proper noun.
   Anton Chekhov   Africa

4. Don't divide contractions or abbreviations.
   can't   o'clock   Ave.   NATO

5. Don't divide the last word of a paragraph or the last word on a page.

A Which of the following words could be divided at the end of a line? Write *Yes* or *No* in the space.

1. space   _____   6. Donna Smith   _____

2. don't   _____   7. FBI   _____

3. traffic   _____   8. away   _____

4. again   _____   9. none   _____

5. nameplate   _____   10. pieces   _____

➤ If a word has a hyphen, divide it at the hyphen.
     self-defense   well-known

B Divide each word into syllables. Use a dictionary if you are not sure.

1. diction   _____   6. background   _____

2. mainstream   _____   7. fireproof   _____

3. teaching   _____   8. magnet   _____

4. self-reliant   _____   9. made-up   _____

5. borrow   _____   10. commit   _____

Decide whether each word should be divided. If it can be divided, divide the word between the appropriate syllables. Write your answer in the space provided.

1. FBI _____

2. custom _____

3. proofread _____

4. pocket _____

5. distance _____

6. name _____

7. Mrs. Wills _____

8. archery _____

9. backbone _____

10. longer _____

11. worthy _____

12. they _____

13. dipper _____

14. wheel _____

15. fortune _____

16. Millie _____

17. tender _____

18. insight _____

19. poster _____

20. South Bend _____

21. computer _____

22. world _____

23. 9 o'clock _____

24. checkbook _____

25. postcard _____

Review Units 6–8

A Rewrite these sentences, adding dashes or ellipses where needed.

1. Did you have you seen my keys anywhere?

   _____

2. Four score and seven years ago dedicated to the proposition that all men are created equal.

   _____

3. I have read this book now torn, tattered, and old to my children and grandchildren.

   _____

4. We look forward to a world founded upon four essential human freedoms. The first is freedom of speech and expression. The fourth is freedom from fear.

   _____

B Add hyphens where needed in these sentences.

5. I have twenty five pledges for the walkathon.

6. The school year ends usually in mid June.

7. Tricia answered with a self assured smile.

8. Velma said that the *Mary Tyler Moore Show* is her all time favorite TV program.

9. Mr. Sedik is an ex player on the school's varsity football team.

10. Ms. Sanchez will compete in the all pro golf tournament.

11. The recipe calls for one half teaspoon of ground ginger.

12. Cheri's grandparents were born in the mid 1940s.

13. The theater shows only G rated films on Saturday afternoons.

14. Some pro British colonists went to Canada during the American Revolution.

C If possible, use a hyphen to divide each word as though you were breaking it at the end of a line. Remember to follow the rules for dividing words.

15. mastery   _____

16. Meryl Streep   _____

17. smoothest   _____

18. beachfront   _____

19. doesn't   _____

20. funnel   _____

Expressions with Parentheses

➤ Parentheses (/) may be used to set off a parenthetical expression or phrase from the rest of the sentence.

➤ The words in parentheses explain an idea or add additional information. Such words are not essential to a sentence and could be omitted.

It was late at night *(well after midnight)* when our car broke down on the deserted highway.

The Browns took their children *(all six of them)* for their doctor's checkup.

Add parentheses to the following sentences where they are needed.

1. Melissa hit the ball using all her strength out of the park.

2. The committee at least four of its members agreed to delay the decision.

3. The bright harvest moon full and round was high in the sky.

4. The team celebrated their victory they had won by two points in the locker room.

5. Mr. Rodriguez smiled broadly as he held his newborn just two-day-old grandchild.

6. Paul looked down at his hands cold and clammy as he stood to give his speech.

7. I read two newspapers I like to keep informed every day.

8. All of the ingredients in the fruit salad apples, bananas, pineapples, etc. are low in calories and nutritious.

9. According to the author see the preface this story is based on a true story.

10. The canned goods that the students collected on their own time will be given to the food pantry.

11. Stan put the old pot dented and dingy in the recycle bin.

12. Shari left precisely at one o'clock for the airport.

For Review: Check out the lesson about using the dash. Dashes can also be used to enclose parenthetical expressions.

Enclosing a Figure or Letter

➤ Use parentheses to enclose numerals or letters that identify items in a list

Students voted for three student council officers: (1) president, (2) vice-president, and (3) secretary.

To make the birdhouse, you need (a) wood, (b) nails, (c) glue, (d) string, and (e) paint.

A Add parentheses where they are needed in the following sentences.

1. My list of chores includes 1 wash the dishes, 2 do the laundry, and 3 vacuum the living room.

2. Remember to a turn off the lights, b lock all the doors, and c take out the garbage when you leave the house.

3. To get to Shari's house, follow these directions: 1 turn left on Jackson Street, 2 go three blocks to Eleventh Street, 3 turn right on Eleventh at Wesley's Restaurant, and 4 walk one-half block to 408 Eleventh Street.

4. The list of school supplies included a six no. 2 pencils, b three folders, c notebook paper, d scissors, e ruler, and f colored markers.

5. Which word means the same as loquacious—a talkative, b sleepy, or c wonderful?

B Write original sentences using parenthetical expressions.

1. _____

_____

2. _____

_____

3. _____

_____

4. _____

_____

5. _____

_____

First Word in a Sentence

➤ Always capitalize the first word in a sentence.
   We went for a long walk in the woods yesterday.

A Read the following paragraph carefully. Capitalize the first word in each sentence.

yesterday was a perfect fall day. the sun shone brightly, and the air had a crisp, clean smell. the trees were painted in gold, red, and brown. who could resist being outdoors on such a beautiful day? i certainly couldn't. i grabbed a sweatshirt and went for a run through the park. after running about twenty minutes, I leaned against a tree and just breathed in the fresh air. it was wonderful!

B Rewrite the following sentences. Capitalize the first word of each sentence. Add marks of punctuation at the end of each one.

in the winter, Larry likes to cross-country ski of all his hobbies, skiing is his favorite it's good, vigorous exercise and helps keep him in shape

_____

_____

_____

_____

Proper Nouns

➤ Always capitalize proper nouns. A proper noun is the name of a particular person, place, thing, or idea.

Person	**Place**	**Thing**
George Washington	New York City	the **U.S.** Constitution
Senator Bradley	Philippine Islands	Empire State Building

➤ Always capitalize the pronoun *I*.

A Capitalize the proper nouns and the pronoun *I* in the following sentences.

1. We crossed the mississippi river near dubuque, iowa.

2. linda's address is 109 bay street, new york, new york.

3. barbara jordan of texas served in the united states congress from 1973 to 1979.

4. "Stop! Stop!" i yelled, but the taxi kept going anyway.

5. We took pictures of trafalgar square in london.

6. i admire the paintings of john singer sargent.

B Capitalize proper nouns and the pronoun *I*.

The national archives is located in washington, d.c. It houses many

valuable records and documents, including the declaration of

independence. When i visited the national archives last september, i

researched information about my great-grandmother, anna marsicek. i

found the 1900 census records for casco, wisconsin, where my great-

grandmother grew up. The census records listed the names, ages, and

occupations of my great-grandmother's brothers and sisters, frank, john,

henry, mary, and julia.

Capitalization Rules

➤ Capitalize geographical names.

Cities, Towns:	Baltimore, Juneau, Denton
Counties:	Montgomery County, Lake County
States:	Pennsylvania, Hawaii, New Mexico
Continents:	North America, Africa, Asia
Countries:	Kenya, Japan, India
Islands:	Philippine Islands, Bermuda
Bodies of Water:	Atlantic Ocean, Lake Erie, Adriatic Sea
Regions:	the South, the Northwest
Streets:	Main Street, Woodhaven Lane, Salem Avenue
Parks:	Yosemite National Park, Watkins State Park

➤ Always capitalize the complete name of a geographical location. Words like *avenue, mountains,* and *river* are capitalized when part of a proper name.

Read the following sentences. Capitalize all the geographical names.

1. Alicia visited glacier national park in montana last year.

2. Several theme parks are in orlando, florida.

3. The jordan river empties into the dead sea.

4. The address is 133 hanford road, burlington, north carolina 27215.

5. Donna has worked in northampton county all of her life.

6. Did you know australia is the only country that is also a continent?

7. Balboa was the first Spaniard to see the pacific ocean.

8. The capital of west virginia is charleston.

9. Lake victoria is the largest lake in africa.

10. The oldest national park in the world is yellowstone national park.

11. The top two wheat-producing countries are china and the united states.

12. The virgin islands are east of puerto rico.

13. Gold seekers and homesteaders settled in the American west.

14. Edmund Hillary and Tenzing Norgay successfully climbed mount everest.

15. The panama canal connects the atlantic ocean to the pacific ocean.

Common Nouns vs Proper Nouns

➤ We capitalize proper nouns but not common nouns. Study the examples below so that you can tell the difference.

Common Noun	**Proper Noun**
I am going to *college* next year.	I will attend Howard Community *College.*
We moved to a different *street.*	Now we live on First *Street.*
He likes to fish in the *river.*	We crossed the Mississippi *River.*

➤ A *proper noun* is the name of a specific place, such as a college or a street.

➤ A *common noun* is the name of a general type of place or location.

■ Look carefully at the words in bold print. Capitalize all proper nouns. Do not capitalize common nouns.

1. Nathaniel was looking for a **hotel** where he could spend the night.

2. We spent the night in the Waldorf Astoria **hotel** in New York City.

3. What **high school** will you be going to next year?

4. I will be going to Ridgeview **high school.**

5. Maria graduated from Boston **college** last December.

6. I can hardly wait until I can go to **college.**

7. We are going to the Roxey **theater** tonight to see a movie.

8. I'm going to the **theater** with Sam tonight.

9. I saw the children running down the **street.**

10. They live on Westley **street.**

11. This bridge crosses the Delaware **river.**

12. What **river** in Africa flows from south to north?

13. An **island** is a body of land completely surrounded by water.

14. We took the ferry to Vancouver **island.**

15. Janet attended the **university** for four years.

16. She attended the **university** of Maryland.

17. We live in Montgomery **county.**

18. Which **county** do you live in?

19. My **aunt** lives in Fort Lauderdale, Florida.

20. The family reunion was held at **aunt** Roxana's house.

Organizations and Dates

Rule One: Capitalize the names of organizations.
Girl Scouts of America   National Broadcasting Company

Rule Two: Capitalize the names of government bodies and agencies.
United States Senate Federal Bureau of Investigation Peace Corps

Rule Three: Capitalize names of important events.
Taste of Chicago   New York Marathon

Rule Four: Capitalize names of holidays, days of the week, and months.
New Year's Day Memorial Day Monday January

 Read the sentences below. Capitalize the proper nouns.

1. The national open golf championship is held in palm springs, california.

2. Megan ran in the boston marathon last year.

3. The civil war was fought in the united states in the 1860s.

4. The members of the united states house of representatives convened on january 3.

5. Who will win the championship in the national football league this year?

6. Many fine programs are shown on the public broadcasting system.

7. Kareem abdul-jabbar played for the national basketball association for many years.

8. Sheilah got a job working for the department of education.

9. The national association for the advancement of colored people was founded in 1908.

10. The rose bowl is the oldest collegiate bowl game.

11. The american heart association works to fight diseases of the heart and blood vessels.

12. The debate team meets on wednesdays after school.

13. The school year usually starts in late august and ends in june.

14. It snowed sixteen inches on veterans day.

15. The flight to phoenix, arizona, left the national airport at 2:05 P.M.

16. We celebrate thanksgiving on the fourth thursday of november.

17. I enjoy national public radio's news programs.

18. In the Northern Hemisphere, winter begins in december and ends in march.

19. clark and pat borden usually have a new year's eve party.

20. The first transcontinental railroad in the united states was built by the union pacific railroad company and the central pacific railroad company.

Proper Adjectives

➤ Capitalize proper adjectives. A proper adjective is an adjective derived from a proper noun.

Noun	Proper Adjective
France	French people
America	American customs

A Write these proper nouns in the form of an adjective. Add a noun after each one. Use a dictionary if necessary.

Example:

Noun	Proper Adjective
Mexico	*Mexican flag*

1. Spain _____

2. Japan _____

3. Canada _____

4. Victoria _____

5. Egypt _____

6. Rome _____

B Capitalize the proper adjectives and nouns in the following sentences.

1. The african elephant has bigger ears and fewer toes than the indian elephant.

2. Casimir Pulaski was a polish hero of the american revolution.

3. Many australian children who live in remote areas are educated through radio correspondence schools.

4. Shakespeare was one of the great writers of the elizabethan era.

5. The month of july was named after the great roman ruler Julius Caesar.

6. The german shepherd can be trained to be an excellent guide dog.

7. The short-haired siamese cat is a popular pet.

8. I think I'll have a ham and swiss cheese sandwich for lunch.

9. The norwegian city of lillehammer hosted the 1994 winter olympic games.

10. The italian flag, with its green, white, and red vertical stripes, was designed by napoleon.

Words in a Title

➤ Capitalize the first word and all important words in the titles of books, stories, magazines, newspapers, movies, poems, songs, documents, and works of art.
  Encyclopedia of American Biography "The Tell-Tale Heart"

➤ Usually you should not capitalize articles (a, an, the) and prepositions (of, on, at) unless they are the first or last words.

A Rewrite these titles. Capitalize all important words.

1. *the wizard of oz* _____

2. mona lisa _____

3. *los angeles times* _____

4. *newsweek* _____

5. *treasure island* _____

6. American bill of rights _____

7. "the scarlet ibis" _____

B Proofread these sentences. Capitalize any important words in the titles.

1. Charles Dickens is the author of *a tale of two cities.*

2. Forty-one Pilgrims signed the mayflower compact in 1620.

3. One of the most widely read newspapers in the country is the *new york times.*

4. Ann's favorite nursery rhyme is "this is the house that jack built."

5. A popular Beatles song in 1967 was "strawberry fields forever."

6. Reruns of the 1950s TV comedy series *i love lucy* can still be seen on TV.

7. The song "can you feel the love tonight" from the movie *the lion king* won the 1994 Academy Award for best original song.

8. The *american magazine* was the first magazine published in the United States.

9. The comic strip "for better or for worse" appears in the *chicago tribune.*

10. In 1995 Sharon Creech's novel *walk two moons* won the Newbery Medal for outstanding children's literature.

Proofreading Practice

A Capitalize each proper noun in the following sentences.

abraham lincoln was the sixteenth president of the united states. Soon after his election, south carolina seceded from the union. Other states followed, and following shots at fort sumter on april 12, 1861, the north and south went to war. The civil war raged for four years until general lee surrendered at appomattox courthouse on april 9, 1865.

On january 1, 1863, lincoln issued the emancipation proclamation. This document stated that all enslaved african americans in states at war with the united states were free. In november of that year, he gave his gettysburg address, perhaps his most famous words, at the dedication of a cemetery for those killed in the battle of gettysburg. Just days after lee's surrender, lincoln attended a performance of *our american cousin* at ford's theatre. There he was assassinated by john wilkes booth. The nation mourned the passing of a great leader. Today many americans think that lincoln was the greatest president the united states ever had.

B Capitalize each proper noun. Also, capitalize the first word in each sentence.

abraham lincoln was an illinois state representative for eight years, but he wanted to do more in politics. in 1847 he got his wish. the people of his district elected him to represent them in the united states congress.

in 1858 lincoln decided to run for a position in the senate. his opponent was senator stephen douglas, the author of the kansas-nebraska act. douglas was a small man in stature but a powerful politician. people called him the "little giant." they called lincoln the "big giant." When lincoln and douglas debated throughout illinois, the people called the debates the battle of the giants. they also called them the great debates. lincoln lost the election, but the debates made him famous.

in 1860 there was an election for president. both lincoln and douglas ran. this time it was abraham lincoln who won. he became the sixteenth president of the united states.

Review Units 9–10

■ Rewrite each sentence, adding parentheses and capital letters where they are needed.

1. the civil war see page 22 began in 1861.

_____

2. In fourth grade, my favorite book was *james and the giant peach* by roald dahl.

_____

3. jackson cold, tired, and anxious paced back and forth as he waited for the bus.

_____

4. The nile river at about 4,180 miles 6,690 kilometers long is the longest river on the earth.

_____

_____

5. in 1996, mel gibson won an academy award for directing the movie *braveheart*.

_____

6. The united nations' peace-keeping forces included american soldiers.

_____

7. insects that go through incomplete metamorphosis go through three stages of life: 1 egg, 2 nymph, and 3 adult.

_____

_____

8. mohandas gandhi helped india gain its independence from great britain.

_____

9. the magazine *george*, published by john f. kennedy, jr., was introduced in september 1995.

_____

_____

10. In the united states, we celebrate thanksgiving day on the fourth thursday of november.

_____

_____

Titles

➤ Italics are letters printed in a slightly sloped way. When you need italics in handwriting, underline the words.

➤ In writing, underline the titles of books, plays, magazines, newspapers, movies, television series, and works of art. In print, such titles would be in italics.

Examples:　　*Little Women*　　　*New York Times*　　　*Whistler's Mother*
　　　　　　　Little Women　　　New York Times　　　Whistler's Mother

■ Underline all the words in the sentences below that should be in italics.

1. While in the doctor's office, I looked through an issue of Sports Illustrated.

2. Every week, Time magazine is delivered to our home.

3. I was reading about The Nutcracker, a ballet that draws huge crowds during the holiday season each year.

4. When we lived in Ohio, we subscribed to the Columbus Dispatch.

5. Have you seen a photograph of Grant Wood's painting American Gothic?

6. My friend Dorothy tried out for the part of Lady Macbeth in the play Macbeth.

7. One of the longest-running Broadway plays is A Chorus Line.

8. The Guinness Book of Records lists many interesting, unusual, and even bizarre records.

9. I found a brief biography of Sojourner Truth in Webster's American Biographies.

10. Slavery through Reconstruction is a mural painted by Aaron Douglas.

11. Robin Williams played an extraterrestrial on the TV series Mork and Mindy.

12. In the 1980s, Harrison Ford starred in the movie Raiders of the Lost Ark and its sequels.

13. The Reader's Digest is the world's most widely read magazine.

14. I'd like to recommend Jack London's best-known book, The Call of the Wild.

15. The opera Madame Butterfly was composed by Giacomo Puccini.

Names and Foreign Words

➤ You should underline the specific names of ships, aircraft, and spacecraft in writing. In print they are put in italics.

Titanic (ocean liner)   *Endeavour* (space shuttle)

➤ Underline the names of legal cases in your writing. You may choose to underline the *v.* (versus), or not, as long as you do so consistently.

Vernonia School District 47J v. *Wayne and Judy Acton*

A Underline the names of ships, aircraft, spacecraft, and legal cases in the following sentences.

1. Charles Lindbergh flew the first solo flight across the Atlantic Ocean in his airplane, the Spirit of St. Louis, in 1927.

2. In 1954 the Supreme Court ruled in Brown v. Board of Education of Topeka that segregated schools were unconstitutional.

3. In 1864 the Confederate submarine Hunley became the first submarine to ever sink a warship.

4. The flight of the space shuttle Discovery was delayed because of woodpecker damage to its fuel-tank insulation.

5. Robert Fulton's Clermont was the first financially successful steamboat.

➤ When you use unfamiliar foreign words or phrases in your writing, be sure to underline them. In print, unfamiliar foreign words or phrases are put in italics. Some foreign words are familiar or commonly used in English. These familiar words are not underlined. Many dictionaries include familiar foreign words that do not have to be underlined.

mañana (tomorrow)   *merci* (thank you)

B Underline any unfamiliar foreign words. Use a dictionary if necessary to determine whether a word is familiar.

1. The ship slipped out of port to shouts of bon voyage from crowds on the dock.

2. Jenny was the fille d'honneur, or maid of honor, at her sister's wedding.

3. The words wir sprechen Deutsch hier on the sign let customers know that the restaurant staff speaks German.

4. When asked if he enjoyed the film, Hector replied that it was good, mas o menos.

5. The fiesta began with a procession through the streets.

Italics can also be used to call special attention to a word, a phrase, or a sentence. It is the writer's choice. When writing, underline the words you want to emphasize.

"What a great game!" the fans exclaimed.

Amanda really *wanted* a CD player.

Underline titles; specific names of ships, aircraft, spacecraft, and legal cases; unfamiliar foreign words; or words that should be emphasized in the following sentences.

1. Maya Angelou told her story about growing up during the Depression in her autobiography I Know Why the Caged Bird Sings.

2. The Wright brothers built and flew Flyer, the first successful airplane, in 1903.

3. In the 1700s, Korin used ink to paint Matsushima on paper-screen panels.

4. In its decision in Marbury v. Madison, the Supreme Court established its right of judicial review.

5. The ships Susan Constant, Discovery, and Godspeed brought the 105 Jamestown settlers to America.

6. During roll call in Spanish class, students give the response aqui to indicate they are present.

7. The storm dumped 23 inches of snow in less than 24 hours.

8. Tom Hanks starred as astronaut Jim Lovell in the movie Apollo 13.

9. Sarah and Annie Elizabeth Delaney published their memoir Having Our Say: The Delaney Sisters' First 100 Years in 1993.

10. Check the time of the program in TV Guide.

11. Donny Osmond has starred as Joseph in a production of Joseph and the Amazing Technicolor Dreamcoat.

12. You might greet an Italian friend with the words come sta.

13. Michelangelo completed the sculpture The Heroic Captive in 1519.

14. With the words "Houston, Tranquility Base here. The Eagle has landed," Neil Armstrong announced that Americans had landed on the moon.

15. In 1995, two Milwaukee, Wisconsin, newspapers merged to become the Milwaukee Journal Sentinel.

Numbers in Sentences

Lesson 1

➤ Write out a number that can be expressed in one or two words.
Joni earns *three hundred* dollars a month.
Karol paid $45.37 for his new jacket.

➤ Write out all numbers that begin a sentence. If the number requires more than two words, rearrange the sentence.
Thirty students went on the field trip.
The bill at the restaurant was $34.89.

Decide whether the numbers in the sentences should be spelled out or written as numerals. Write out the numbers if necessary. If no changes are needed, write "Correct" in the space.

Example:
Seven
~~7~~ students worked on the project together.

_____ 1. Congress has 2 houses—the Senate and the House of Representatives.

_____ 2. Lea got 11 phone calls last night!

_____ 3. The actress has performed in 123 movies.

_____ 4. My great-uncle was 91 years old on his last birthday.

_____ 5. The candidate won by 1,230 votes.

_____ 6. This shirt costs $61.24 with tax.

_____ 7. There were 22 players on the softball team roster.

_____ 8. "3 students got A's on the test," the teacher said.

_____ 9. 13 is considered a baker's dozen.

_____ 10. Costa Rica has a population of about 3,424,000.

_____ 11. The Senate has 100 members.

_____ 12. I spent $3.69 at the fast-food restaurant.

_____ 13. I checked 3 books out of the library.

_____ 14. She ran the marathon in a little over 5 hours.

_____ 15. Aaron placed $5,631.32 in the company's safe.

Ordinal Numbers

➤ In most cases, write out ordinal numbers in sentences.

1st	first	7th	seventh	13th	thirteenth
2nd	second	8th	eighth	20th	twentieth
3rd	third	9th	ninth	21st	twenty-first
4th	fourth	10th	tenth	30th	thirtieth
5th	fifth	11th	eleventh	100th	one hundredth
6th	sixth	12th	twelfth	1000th	one thousandth

Examples: Libby had the *sixth* highest score.
Claude just had his *fourteenth* birthday.

■ Write the ordinal numbers as words in the space provided.

_____ 1. On his 16th birthday, Reiko got his driver's permit.

_____ 2. John Adams was the 2nd president of the United States.

_____ 3. Saliha was the 5th student to apply for the scholarship.

_____ 4. Our team is in 4th place.

_____ 5. The 12th grade is the final year of high school.

_____ 6. 65th Street is four blocks west.

_____ 7. George Washington was "1st in war, 1st in peace, and 1st in the hearts of his countrymen."

_____ 8. In 1912, Theodore Roosevelt ran for president as a 3rd-party candidate.

_____ 9. I have study hall during the 6th period.

_____ 10. This is the 10th edition of this dictionary.

_____ 11. I was the 9th person to cross the finish line.

_____ 12. In 1976, the United States celebrated the 200th anniversary of the Declaration of Independence.

More about Numbers

➤ If one of the numbers in a series requires figures, then use figures for all of the numbers.

> Miko spent $1.75 on a sandwich and $1.00 for fruit juice.

➤ Normally, write fractions as words.

> *One-third* of the pie was missing.

➤ Always use figures for decimals.

> Sam has a fever of *101.4* degrees.

➤ For percentages, use figures followed by the word *percent*.

> Hank scored *88 percent* on his math test.

■ Decide whether the numbers in the sentences should be written out or in numerals. Rewrite the numbers if necessary. If no changes are needed, write "Correct" on the answer line.

_____ 1. The slogan says the soap is ninety-nine percent pure.

_____ 2. 13 people came to the party at Trong's house.

_____ 3. The outfit costs $29.95 for the shirt, forty dollars for the pants, and $68.00 for the sweater.

_____ 4. The candidate was chosen by more than 1/2 of the voters.

_____ 5. The stock prices dropped by twelve percent in one day.

_____ 6. The rope is 12.4 feet long.

_____ 7. Zosia had a temperature of one hundred one point nine degrees.

_____ 8. 4 months ago the Thomas family moved into their new house.

_____ 9. Christy grew 3/4 of an inch last month.

_____ 10. The check was for $83.59 including tax.

_____ 11. Normal body temperature is 98.6 degrees.

_____ 12. He paid fifty-two dollars and twenty cents for the shirt.

Numbers in Addresses and Dates

➤ Use figures when writing numbers in an address, a time of day, or a date.
Gail lives at 85 Oak Avenue.
Tanya was born on November 22, 1971.
Pedro opens the office at 8:30 A.M. every day.

12 ■ Choose the correct style for the numbers in parentheses. Write your answer in the space provided.

_____ 1. The first day of school was September (2, second).

_____ 2. This crossword puzzle has (114, one hundred fourteen) clues.

_____ 3. (4, Four) weeks ago today we were on vacation.

_____ 4. More than (80, eighty) percent of the students got an A on the test.

_____ 5. The party lasted (2, two) hours.

_____ 6. On December (3, third), 1775, John Paul Jones first raised the American flag on a navy ship.

_____ 7. This boat could travel at (65, sixty-five) miles an hour.

_____ 8. Quincy lives on (5th, Fifth) Avenue in New York City.

_____ 9. The party starts at (8, eight) P.M.

_____ 10. Kelly runs (2 1/2, two and a half) miles every day.

_____ 11. I live at (31, thirty-one) Jersey Avenue.

_____ 12. (3, Three) students were left at the school.

_____ 13. You may buy (1/2, one-half) of that cake for five dollars.

_____ 14. The auditorium held (200, two hundred) people.

_____ 15. The first class begins at (9:05 A.M., five minutes after nine).

_____ 16. We must mail (369, three hundred sixty-nine) letters by next week.

_____ 17. Our garden is (3/4, three-fourths) of an acre.

_____ 18. Jessica had saved ($15, fifteen) dollars in pennies.

Read the sentences carefully. Correct any errors you find. The first one is done for you.

third

My parents moved into the ~~3rd~~ house from the corner on January

sixteenth, nineteen hundred and seventy-three. Ever since then they have

lived at sixty-one Maple Street. At the time, they paid seventy-two

thousand five hundred dollars for the house. Now they are selling it for

$295,000.

They have decided to spend 1/2 of the year in an apartment here and

the rest of the year in Arizona. Mom and Dad are looking forward to

winter temperatures in the 60s and 70s.

I for 1 will miss the old house on Maple Street. After all, I spent 2/3 of

my life there. The house was in a perfect location for a kid. School was 4

blocks away and the park just three blocks away. I could even walk to the

library, which was only one point five miles away. I used to spend fifty

percent of my free time at the park or the library. However, now I'm grown

and my two children are excited about their grandparents' move. They

can't wait to travel two thousand three hundred fifty miles to visit

Grandma and Grandpa during winter vacation next year. They're looking

forward to a sunny and warm vacation. As a matter of fact, so am I!

Review Units 11–12

A Underline the titles of books, plays, newspapers, movies, television programs, and works of art in these sentences.

1. The movie Babe is about an orphan piglet.

2. Have you read The Diary of Anne Frank?

3. In 1995, these programs were the most-watched television series: Seinfeld, E.R., Home Improvement, and Grace under Fire.

4. The Highland Park News is my hometown newspaper.

5. The new productions of the musicals Showboat and Carousel played in Chicago in the spring of 1996.

6. The artist Christo specializes in temporary artworks such as The Umbrellas, Japan-U.S.A.

7. I researched information about cholesterol in the American Medical Journal.

8. The movie Braveheart received the 1996 Academy Award for best picture.

9. You can find a copy of the Wall Street Journal at the library.

10. Laura plays the part of Dorothy in our school's production of The Wiz.

B In the space provided, write the correct form of the number.

_____ 1. The top candidate received (55, fifty-five) percent of the vote.

_____ 2. I spent ($25.65, twenty-five dollars and sixty-five cents) at the fair.

_____ 3. Teresa had a temperature of (102.3, one hundred two point three) degrees.

_____ 4. The crowd filled about (5/6ths, five-sixths) of the stadium.

_____ 5. (100, One hundred) pennies equals ($1, one dollar).

_____ 6. Noah has a (3.9, three point nine) grade point average.

_____ 7. Tax day is on April (15, fifteen) every year.

_____ 8. The store opens at (9:00, nine) A.M.

Understanding Syllables

➤ A syllable is a part of a word that has one vowel sound. A word can have one syllable or many syllables.

    try   (one syllable)

    trying try • ing   (two syllables)

➤ The vowels are: *a, e, i, o, u.*

    All the other letters are consonants.

➤ *Y* can also be a vowel when it sounds like *e* or *i.*

Y as a consonant	*Y* as a vowel
young	baby
yet	cry

Count the syllables in each of these words. Write the number in the space. You may use a dictionary.

_____	1. sharper	_____	16. power
_____	2. shopper	_____	17. tiny
_____	3. consonant	_____	18. biography
_____	4. record	_____	19. Marie
_____	5. February	_____	20. television
_____	6. someone	_____	21. flirting
_____	7. year	_____	22. plant
_____	8. beach	_____	23. Nancy
_____	9. window	_____	24. dictionary
_____	10. lamp	_____	25. perfection
_____	11. planted	_____	26. word
_____	12. ruler	_____	27. sheep
_____	13. vowel	_____	28. popcorn
_____	14. holder	_____	29. America
_____	15. perfectly	_____	30. lunchroom

When to Drop the Final -e

➤ When a word ends with a silent *e,* you must make a decision before adding an ending. Do you keep the *e* or do you drop it? There are two rules to help you decide.

Rule One: Words that end with silent *e* keep the *e* before an ending that begins with a consonant.

improve + -ment   improvement   use + -ful   useful

Rule Two: Words that end with a silent *e* drop the *e* before an ending that begins with a vowel. Remember: *y* is a vowel when it sounds like *e* or *i.*

improve + -ing   improving   use + -ed   used

 Add an ending to each of the following words. Write the new word.

Example: write + -*er*   writer

1. admire + -ed   _____

2. taste + -y   _____

3. exchange + -ing   _____

4. hope + -ful   _____

5. lone + -ly   _____

6. excite + -ment   _____

7. compare + -able   _____

8. emote + -ion   _____

9. time + -less   _____

10. believe + -able   _____

11. arrange + -ment   _____

12. bore + -dom   _____

13. peace + -ful   _____

14. style + -ish   _____

15. large + -est   _____

Doubling the Final Consonant

➤ Sometimes we double the final consonant before we add an ending.
Sometimes we don't. Here is one rule you can follow.

Rule One: When a one-syllable word ends in a single consonant, and there is
only one vowel before that consonant, double the consonant before adding an
ending that begins with a vowel.

stop + -ed = sto**pp**ed   red + -est = re**dd**est

 Study the following list of words. Circle all of the words that have
these characteristics:
> ➤ one syllable.
> ➤ "single" consonant ending.
> ➤ only "one" vowel before the final consonant.

1. swim	8. jump	15. boat
2. sing	9. plan	16. clear
3. sweep	10. hem	17. ship
4. love	11. bat	18. top
5. stir	12. beet	19. red
6. run	13. drum	20. slip
7. drop	14. hurt	21. grab

B Add the ending to each of the following words. Double the final
consonant if the word follows the rule above.

Example: run + -er   runner

1. plan	+	-er	_____
2. wrap	+	-ed	_____
3. hem	+	-ing	_____
4. slip	+	-ery	_____
5. hot	+	-est	_____
6. sweet	+	-er	_____
7. fun	+	-y	_____
8. hop	+	-ing	_____
9. look	+	-ing	_____
10. big	+	-er	_____

Words with Two Syllables

Rule Two: When a word with two syllables is accented on the last syllable and it ends in a single consonant preceded by a single vowel, double the consonant before adding an ending which begins with a vowel.

Say these two words: *begin*   *color*
>   *Begin is* accented on the "last" syllable.
>   *Color is* accented on the "first" syllable.
Can you hear the difference?

A Study the following list of words. Circle all of the words that have these characteristics:
> ➤ more than one syllable.
> ➤ "single" consonant ending.
> ➤ "one" vowel before the final consonant.
> ➤ accent on the last syllable.

1. number	6. occur	11. wonder
2. admit	7. travel	12. record
3. teach	8. offer	13. forgot
4. parrot	9. equip	14. control
5. limit	10. forget	15. perfect

B Read the ending to each word. Double the final consonant if the word follows the rule above.

1. number   +   -ing   _____

2. admit   +   -ance   _____

3. teach   +   -er   _____

4. parrot   +   -ed   _____

5. limit   +   -ing   _____

6. occur   +   -ence   _____

7. travel   +   -er   _____

8. offer   +   -ed   _____

9. equip   +   -ment   _____

10. forget   +   -ing   _____

i before *e* except after *c*

Rule: Put the *i* before *e* except after *c* or when sounded like *a* as in *neighbor* and *weigh.*

i before *e*	except after *c*	or when sounded like *a*
believe	receive	neighborhood

Naturally, every rule has exceptions, and here are some.

foreign	height	either
seize	ancient	leisure

Circle the correct spelling of each word. Write the correct spelling in the space.

1. friend   freind   _____

2. frieght   freight   _____

3. weight   wieght   _____

4. ceiling   cieling   _____

5. piece   peice   _____

6. acheive   achieve   _____

7. vien   vein   _____

8. shriek   shreik   _____

9. theif   thief   _____

10. deceive   decieve   _____

11. grief   greif   _____

12. brief   breif   _____

13. feild   field   _____

14. niether   neither   _____

15. veil   viel   _____

16. relieve   releive   _____

17. reciept   receipt   _____

18. yeild   yield   _____

19. cheif   chief   _____

20. seige   siege   _____

Change the *y* to *i* and Add *-es*

➤ When a word ends in *y* and you want to add an *s*, just follow the rules below.

Rule One: If the letter before the *y* is a consonant, change the *y* to *i* and add *-es*.
baby   babies
story   stories

Rule Two: If the word ends in *y* but the letter before the *y* is a vowel, just add *-s*.
toy   toys
monkey   monkeys

 Make each word below plural using the rules above. Write the correct spelling in the space.

1. army   _____

2. butterfly   _____

3. attorney   _____

4. party   _____

5. copy   _____

6. sky   _____

7. battery   _____

8. city   _____

9. journey   _____

10. key   _____

11. guy   _____

12. pulley   _____

13. day   _____

14. valley   _____

15. library   _____

16. country   _____

17. lullaby   _____

18. quality   _____

19. tray   _____

20. boundary   _____

Irregular Plurals

➤ A singular noun names one person, place, thing, or idea. A plural noun names more than one person, place, thing, or idea.

Rule One: Ordinarily, you add -s to form a plural.
one computer   many computers

A Write the plural of each word in the space.

1. glove _____
2. record _____
3. rule _____
4. number _____
5. meal _____
6. house _____

7. page _____
8. ticket _____
9. plural _____
10. paper _____
11. model _____
12. bridge _____

Rule Two: Add -es to form plurals of words ending in s, sh, ch, x, and z.
one bus   two buses   one speech   many speeches

B Write the plural of these words in the space.

1. class _____
2. watch _____
3. dish _____
4. box _____
5. wish _____
6. guess _____

7. ax _____
8. beach _____
9. waltz _____
10. tax _____
11. atlas _____
12. reflex _____

➤ Form the plural of a hyphenated compound word by adding -s to the main word.

    Right: brothers-in-law
    Wrong: brother-in-laws

Rule Three: When a word ends in *f* or *fe*, make it plural by changing the *f* to *v* and adding *-s* or *-es*. There are exceptions, so check a dictionary to be sure.

        leaf   leaves   *but*   belief   beliefs

C Write the plural of these words in the space. Use a dictionary to check the words.

1. calf	_____	6. giraffe	_____
2. wolf	_____	7. chief	_____
3. knife	_____	8. gulf	_____
4. roof	_____	9. shelf	_____
5. cliff	_____	10. life	_____

Rule Four: A few words are "very irregular." There is no rule that works all the time. You must learn these separately.

child	children	man	men	woman	women
tooth	teeth	moose	moose	goose	geese
deer	deer	foot	feet	mouse	mice

D Write the plural of these words in the space. Use a dictionary to check the words.

1. screech	_____	11. goose	_____
2. glass	_____	12. child	_____
3. spy	_____	13. signal	_____
4. wolf	_____	14. stage	_____
5. handkerchief	_____	15. chimney	_____
6. gentleman	_____	16. deer	_____
7. mess	_____	17. border	_____
8. match	_____	18. reef	_____
9. wall	_____	19. delay	_____
10. lady	_____	20. belief	_____

Read the following paragraphs carefully. Look for spelling mistakes. Correct any errors that you find.

Family Night

Our school is haveing its Family Night next week. All the studentes and their familys are invited to take part. At the begining of the evening, there is a potluck supper. My dad bakeed chicken for the supper. I can't wait to have some. His chicken is always tastey.

After supper, three classs are puting on several short plaies. We were able to choose the play we wanted to be in. I prefered to be in the play about Pilgrims.

In the play, my freind and I use toy axs to cut down trees. Some kids build cabines. Others plant corn in fields we clearred. Finally, we celebrate Thanksgiving. All the Pilgrim womans, men, and childs work together to make dinner. While some of us are useing knifes to carve turkeys, others are serving gooses and corn. We also serve berrys and bread. I beleive people will like our play.

After the plays, familyies take a breif tour of the classrooms. Every family recieves a bookmark made by a student. Then we all say goodnight and go home.

Contractions and Possessive Pronouns

➤ A homophone is a word that sounds exactly like another word. Its meaning and spelling are different.

➤ Important: Possessive pronouns never have apostrophes.

it's	contraction for it is or it has	It's a huge dog.
its	possessive pronoun	Its leash is over there.
you're	contraction for you are	You're wearing a winter jacket.
your	possessive pronoun	Your jacket looks warm.
they're	contraction for they are	They're arriving at eight.
their	possessive pronoun	Their bus arrives at eight.
who's	contraction for who is	Who's sitting here?
whose	possessive pronoun	Whose seat is this?

Write the correct word in the space.

1. The puppy is whimpering. I think _____ hungry. (it's, its)

2. Where is _____ food? (it's, its)

3. I wonder what _____ name is? (it's, its)

4. Did you hear that car? _____ muffler needs fixing. (It's, Its)

5. Where are his shoes? I think _____ missing. (they're, their)

6. See that coat? _____ is it? (Who's, Whose)

7. We are here to see our team. We hope _____ going to win. (they're, their)

8. Where are _____ mittens? (you're, your)

9. If you don't hurry, _____ going to be late. (you're, your)

10. "_____ there?" asked Calvin. (Who's, Whose)

11. Is this _____ report? (you're, your)

12. Where is _____ apartment? (they're their)

13. _____ story should we read next? (Who's, Whose)

14. Terryl is the only player _____ still here. (who's, whose)

15. _____ due to arrive at 4:15. (They're, Their)

Read the sets of commonly misspelled words.

to—a preposition (I'm going to the movies.)
too—very; also (I'm going, too.)
two—a number (I would like two pieces.)

hear—receive a sound through the ears (I hear music!)
here—this place (Put the book here.)

past—a former time (History is the story of the past.)
passed—past tense of the verb *pass.* (She passed the vegetables to her brother.)

through—in one side and out the other (Go through the door.)
threw—past tense of *throw* (She threw the ball.)

their—possessive pronoun (Their car is in the garage.)
there—in that place (Park the car over there.)
they're—contraction for they are (They're washing the car.)

principal—the main one (The Mississippi is the principal river of America.)
principal—the head of a school (Mr. Taylor is the principal of our school.)
principal—the amount of money someone borrows (The principal of the loan
　　　　was $2,000.)
principle—a basic truth; a rule of conduct (Cheating is against Tom's principles.)

Choose the correct word and write it in the space.

1. Ms. Sparks is the _____ of the school. (principal, principle)

2. The shortstop _____ the ball to first base. (threw, through)

3. Rena and Rob took _____ children to the park. (there, they're, their)

4. I'm _____ tired to play ball right now. (to, too, two)

5. The recipe calls for _____ cups of flour. (to, too, two)

6. For the _____ three years, we have lived in North Dakota. (past, passed)

7. Baltimore is a _____ city in Maryland. (principal, principle)

8. One of my _____ is to be honest in all my dealings with people. (principals, principles)

9. Did you _____ that thunder? (hear, here)

10. I left my books _____ and my sweater over there. (hear, here)

11. We _____ the fire station on our way to the store. (past, passed)

12. Jimbo likes to work on the computer, and Tessa does, _____. (to, too, two)

Words That Sound or Look Almost Alike

➤ There are many words in English that sound or look almost alike. The meaning may be alike or very different. They are easier to spell if you pronounce them correctly.

advice (noun) an opinion someone gives to another person about what to do
   My advice is to stay inside until the storm is over.
advise (verb) to give your opinion to another person.
   Mike advised Sally to leave early.

probable (adjective) likely to happen
   Six inches of snow is probable today.
probably (adverb) likely to happen
   It will probably snow today.

than (conjunction) a word used to introduce a comparison
   I am taller than Gerry.
then (adverb) at that time; soon after
   At first I was cold; then I warmed up by the fire.

quiet (adjective) still; calm; motionless
   The children were quiet during the show.
quite (adverb) completely; entirely
   Lunch is not quite ready yet.

accept (verb) to receive willingly
   I am pleased to accept the nomination.
except (preposition) leaving out; other than
   Everyone was there except Henri.

Write the correct word in the space.

1. It was so _____ you could hear a pin drop. (quiet, quite)

2. I am _____ pleased to meet you. (quiet, quite)

3. Please _____ this gift. (accept, except)

4. Everyone _____ Andre plans to go to the meeting. (accept, except)

5. I read the book first; _____ I saw the movie. (than, then)

6. Francie is two inches taller _____ Don. (than, then)

7. Kelly _____ will score fifteen points in tonight's game. (probable, probably)

8. The weather report indicated that rain is _____. (probable, probably)

9. I would like your _____ about which course to take. (advice, advise)

10. Your counselor will _____ you about which course to take. (advice, advise)

Proofreading Practice

Extra! Extra! Use a dictionary to look up the meaning of these homophones: weather, whether; break, brake; plain, plane; their, there; allowed, aloud; weight, wait.

 Proofread the following paragraphs. Correct any errors you find.

The whether reports announced that their would be only too to four inches of snow. By noon, however, it became plane that the storm was bigger then expected. The principle called the superintendent for advise about weather to send the students home. The superintendent recommended that the school be closed and the children be sent home.

The principal aloud everyone to go home accept the children who ride Bus 52. There bus was in the repair shop for work on its breaks. They would have to weight for another bus to complete its route and than return to the school two pick them up. Six hours later the children were still waiting. They played ball, studied, and watched television.

The principal and two teachers decided that it would probable be best for the children to stay overnight at the school. Some students were anxious to get home, but others excepted the overnight stay as an adventure. They ate dinner in the cafeteria, and than everyone spent the night in the gym. It was like a huge slumber party. When asked about their night in school, the students said that it was okay. One student said, however, "If you think your going to have to spend the night in school, I would advice you to bring a pillow."

Review Units 13–14

Read each sentence. Choose the word in parentheses that is correctly spelled and write it in the space provided.

_____ 1. Ira is taking (swimming, swiming) lessons.

_____ 2. I can't find two of the puzzle (peices, pieces).

_____ 3. Maryland has twenty-three (countys, counties).

_____ 4. Two (halfs, halves) equal a whole.

_____ 5. We need hall (passes, passis) to leave the classroom.

_____ 6. Our team needs only seven more (victories, victorys) to be in the playoffs.

_____ 7. The dog has been (diging, digging) in the garden again.

_____ 8. We saw bears and moose as we drove (threw, through) the park.

_____ 9. He can lift fifty-pound (weights, wieghts).

_____ 10. Is Anna Marie coming, (to, too)?

_____ 11. My sister is four years older (then, than) I am.

_____ 12. According to the saying, cats have nine (lives, lifes).

_____ 13. Some farmers raise (turkeies, turkeys).

_____ 14. Do you want to go (shoping, shopping) with me?

_____ 15. Are you (quiet, quite) sure this is the right address?

_____ 16. Jorge found the (receipt, reciept) for the shirt he bought.

_____ 17. The dogs are barking, but (they're, their) noise does not bother me.

_____ 18. The flower (arrangment, arrangement) is Karen's work.

_____ 19. The travel books are on those (shelves, shelfs).

_____ 20. Tania (admited, admitted) that she had made a mistake.

_____ 21. The politician said he would keep his speech (breif, brief).

_____ 22. The victory parade (passed, past) by crowds of waving, cheering people.

_____ 23. Is there a rule (limiting, limitting) the number of bags you can carry onto the plane?

_____ 24. I have been (admiring, admireing) the painting by Renoir.

_____ 25. She put honey in her tea to make it (sweetter, sweeter).

End-of-Book Test

Punctuation

A In each item, choose the sentence that is correctly punctuated.

_____ 1. Anita have you been to the amusement park in Gurnee Illinois

_____   **a.** Anita, have you been to the amusement park in Gurnee, Illinois.

_____   **b.** Anita have you been to the amusement park, in Gurnee Illinois?

_____   **c.** Anita, have you been to the amusement park in Gurnee, Illinois?

_____ 2. February has twenty eight days it has twenty nine in a leap year

_____   **a.** February has twenty-eight days, it has twenty nine in a leap year.

_____   **b.** February has twenty-eight days; it has twenty-nine in a leap year.

_____   **c.** February has twenty eight days; it has twenty-nine in a leap year.

_____ 3. Amazing For the very first time he arrived at 900 A M exactly

_____   **a.** Amazing! For the very first time, he arrived at 9:00 A. M. exactly.

_____   **b.** Amazing, For the very first time he arrived at 9;00 A M exactly.

_____   **c.** Amazing! For the very first time he arrived at 9:00 AM. exactly.

_____ 4. Joe cant find his right shoe however he did find the left one

_____   **a.** Joe cant find his right shoe, however he did find the left one.

_____   **b.** Joe can't find his right shoe, however, he did find the left one.

_____   **c.** Joe can't find his right shoe; however, he did find the left one.

B Rewrite each sentence, adding appropriate punctuation where needed.

1. My sister in law a university professor studies childrens early development

_____

_____

2. Dr. Adams asked Have you had measles mumps or chicken pox Ms Takei

_____

_____

3. I have a list where is it of things to buy milk bread cat food and cereal

_____

_____

_____

4. She said By the way Im leaving for London England on Friday March 19

_____

_____

Capitalization

C Read each sentence. Circle each letter that should be a capital letter.

1. The letter was addressed to ms. joy renault, 657 ivy st., st. louis, mo 63105.

2. the first president of the sierra club was john muir.

3. After i saw the movie _sense and sensibility,_ i read the book by jane austen.

4. todd mitchell is playing the part of toad in the play _the wind in the willows._

5. In 1215 the english barons forced king john to sign the magna carta.

6. The white house is located at 1600 pennsylvania avenue.

7. some states celebrate presidents' day on the third monday in february.

8. janice and i are studying french literature and greek mythology.

9. In july the frasers moved from detroit, michigan, to miami, florida.

10. The rockville jazz festival will be held at riverside park in late august.

Spelling

D Read each sentence. Choose the word in parentheses that is correctly spelled and write it in the space provided.

_____ 1. David is always (forgeting, forgetting) his gym bag.

_____ 2. When the ticket office opened, I was (fifteenth, 15th) in line.

_____ 3. Alix, it is (you're, your) turn to choose a movie.

_____ 4. Water dripped slowly from the (cieling, ceiling) of the room.

_____ 5. In the woods, we saw deer, badgers, and (foxes, foxs).

_____ 6. Did I (hear, here) you say that you are going to France?

_____ 7. (40, Forty) people signed up for the bus trip to the museum.

_____ 8. Young children like to listen to the same (stories, storys) over and over.

_____ 9. Is that corn or soybeans growing in that (field, feild)?

_____ 10. The (leafs, leaves) of that maple turn bright red in the fall.